Mental Illness

ISSUES FOR THE NINETIES

Volume 21

Editor

Craig Donnellan

First published by Independence
PO Box 295
Cambridge CB1 3XP

British Library Cataloguing in Publication Data
Mental Illness – (Issues for the Nineties Series)
I. Donnellan, Craig II. Series
362.2

ISBN 1 86168 033 3

Printed in Great Britain
City Print Ltd,
Milton Keynes

Typeset by
Claire Boyd

Cover
The illustration on the front cover is by
Andrew Smith.

CONTENTS

Chapter One: What is mental illness?

Mental illness	1
Mental health and the young	3
Help! I'm losing control	5
Mental health problems – what do they mean?	7
Hidden signs of a depressed child	9
'Crisis out of a drama' on unstable children	9
That old shrinking feeling	10
Suicidal behaviour in children and young people	12
Understanding depression	14
Depression in the workplace	16
Not just sticks and stones	18
The baby blues and postnatal depression	20
Mental health and older people	21
Drug that can ease the misery of Alzheimer's	23

Dementia in perspective	23
Alzheimer's disease – what is it?	24
Can you tell me something about schizophrenia?	26
Living with schizophrenia	28

Chapter Two: Seeking help

Mental illness	31
SANE	33
What are child and adolescent psychiatrists?	34
How to help someone who is suicidal	35
Index	38
Additional resources	39
Acknowledgements	40

Introduction

Mental Illness is the twenty-first volume in the series:
Issues For The Nineties. The aim of this series is to offer up-to-date information about important issues in our world.

Mental Illness looks at the many different problems associated with mental illness as well as exploring the types of help available.

The information comes from a wide variety of sources and includes:
Government reports and statistics
Newspaper reports and features
Magazine articles and surveys
Literature from lobby groups
and charitable organisations.

It is hoped that, as you read about the many aspects of the issues explored in this book, you will critically evaluate the information presented. It is important that you decide whether you are being presented with facts or opinions. Does the writer give a biased or an unbiased report? If an opinion is being expressed, do you agree with the writer?

Mental Illness offers a useful starting-point for those who need convenient access to information about the many issues involved. However, it is only a starting-point. At the back of the book is a list of organisations which you may want to contact for further information.

*****

Mental illness

What does it mean?

What is mental illness?

Just like physical illness, mental illness involves a wide range of problems and complaints. There are many different types of mental illness. Often these involve feelings of depression, anxiety and confusion – all of which most people get at some time or other, particularly after a distressing life event such as a bereavement. But with mental illness these feelings occur to such an extent or for such a long period of time that they make it very difficult for a person to cope with everyday life.

Thanks to research into mental illness, there are now reliable definitions of the different types of mental illness and ways of measuring their severity and development. Our greater knowledge and understanding of mental illness allows us to investigate and treat it more effectively.

What is a 'nervous breakdown'?

If you hear that someone has had a 'nervous breakdown', you would normally understand that to mean that they cannot cope with the pressures of their everyday life. In fact, however, it is a term rarely used by mental health professionals because it is too imprecise. They would need to make a much more detailed and specific diagnosis in order to plan appropriate treatments.

What causes mental illness?

All of us have certain psychological strengths and weaknesses. These are determined by our personalities, previous life experiences, the genes that we inherit and probably some physical characteristics of our nervous system. We also have a number of external social supports such as our family, friends and carers who protect us from life's stresses and strains.

Most mental health problems seem to occur as a result of events that happen to us and our difficulty in coping with them at the time. We may become particularly vulnerable at a specific time, for example, because of a bereavement or loss of a job. In these circumstances we normally experience emotional distress and some of us develop conditions like depression or schizophrenia. The way that others help and respond to the situation can be very important in bringing about recovery.

How common is mental illness?

Mental illness severe enough to need professional assistance is as common as heart disease and three times as common as cancer. One in ten people suffer from it and up to one in five children. Over 91 million working days were lost in 1990/91 due to sickness absence certified as mental disorder. Compare this figure to the 800,000 days lost in 1991 owing to strikes. Over 5,500 people commit suicide each year – more than the number who die in road traffic accidents. Most people who commit suicide are suffering from mental illness at the time.

Psychosis

People often use the word 'psychotic' to mean very angry or irrational. But what it really means is that your ability to distinguish between what is real and what is imaginary is seriously affected.

So if you were psychotic, you might hear people saying things when no one is speaking – 'hearing voices' which sound quite real to you. Or you might develop strong persistent beliefs or 'delusions' which are unbelievable to others around you who know you well.

Does anyone ever really recover from being psychotic?

At some stage in their lives many people develop psychotic symptoms – perhaps when they are very depressed or physically ill or misusing alcohol or drugs – and recover fully. It is also possible to recover completely from schizophrenia, even when a sufferer has had the symptoms for many years. For some people, however, the symptoms do persist or return. What is important is that the symptoms are recognised and the appropriate treatment given. Prompt action can significantly reduce the distressing and disabling effects of psychosis.

Neurosis

Neurosis is a broad term used to describe anxiety and depression. The word has been used in such a vague way for so long that it is being used less and less by mental health professionals.

Specific mental illnesses

Schizophrenia

Schizophrenia is a condition that affects the most basic mental functions that give people their sense of individuality, uniqueness and direction. It can cause them to hallucinate (e.g. hear voices), develop feelings of bewilderment and fear, and believe that their deepest thoughts, feelings and acts may be known to, or controlled by, others.

What is it like to have schizophrenia?

If you can imagine how it must feel to hear someone abusing or criticising you for hours on end only to find that nobody is there, then you can begin to understand what it is like to suffer from schizophrenia. Or you may feel that whatever you do or wherever you go, someone is following or persecuting you or controlling your thoughts and actions for reasons you cannot understand.

If you try to tell someone about what is happening to you – even close family and friends – they may look at you strangely and dismiss what you say. They may even become frightened and distance themselves from you. Not surprisingly, you may also become withdrawn and lethargic.

Manic-depressive illness

Manic-depressive illness causes profound changes in mood, from severe depression and lethargy, to elation and over-activity.

Lots of people get mood swings – does that make them manic-depressive?

Most people have changes in mood, ranging from feeling low and depressed through to being calm and contented and excited or very happy. Manic-depression, however, involves extreme mood swings which significantly affect a person's ability to function, concentrate and participate in their normal personal relationships.

You may feel profoundly depressed for lengthy periods or so elated and excited that your judgement and behaviour are affected. You might seriously overestimate your capabilities so that you make decisions or act in ways that you deeply regret later. You may believe yourself to be someone you are not, and even hear messages or interpret innocent comments which, to you, confirm this belief. You may feel so full of energy that you eventually exhaust yourself and others around you, and when people try to 'bring you back to earth', you get irritated and impatient with them.

Depressive disorder

A depressive disorder is a condition in which feelings like depression, loss of interest, reduced energy, suicidal thoughts, and sleep and appetite disturbance go beyond normal mood changes.

Doesn't everyone get depressed?

Most of us get depressed from time to time but we can usually relate it to an event in our lives and find a way of relieving it. But if you become severely depressed, life becomes unremittingly bleak and despair clouds all your thoughts and actions. Drive and motivation dissolve and life generally seems meaningless. Sleep is often the only escape, but you may have difficulty actually falling asleep and then wake early, feeling even more desperate. You can feel guilty in quite a disproportionate way and hopeless about things ever improving. In the end, suicide may seem the only way out.

What about children?

Even children get depressed, but they are more likely to talk about feeling miserable or fed-up or bored. Sometimes they may say that they wish they were dead. Young adolescents often feel miserable, but when they get depressed they may become withdrawn and stay in their room. Depression may affect their performance at school. Alternatively, they may become angry a lot, or cry, or say that they are no good. They may start to misuse alcohol or drugs.

Anxiety states

Anxiety states include phobic, panic and general anxiety disorders in which anxiety symptoms, such as worry, tension, over-breathing and giddiness cause significant distress and disability.

Anxiety is very unpleasant. However, understanding and tackling the cause of anxiety can make it more tolerable. For many of us, a certain level of anxiety is accepted as necessary in order to perform well when faced with specific challenges, for example, a job interview.

In fact, avoiding situations that cause anxiety can limit your life considerably. In more extreme cases, phobias will lead us to avoid certain situations, such as flying in an aeroplane. 'Facing the fear' is essential if it is to be overcome.

Dementia

Dementia leads to a decline in a person's intellectual functioning and memory. People can become very confused. Their memory for current events is impaired but they are often able to recall scenes from many years ago with great clarity.

Isn't dementia just an effect of old age?
Most people lose at least a small part of their memory as they grow older. However, dementia is not just an effect of old age but involves specific changes in the brain caused usually by Alzheimer's disease or blood vessel disease.

Dementia is rare in people under 65 but becomes more common with increasing age. Twenty % of people over 80 are affected.

Eating disorders

Eating disorders include anorexia nervosa, a condition that leads to severe weight loss, and bulimia nervosa, a condition that combines over-eating with vomiting or 'purging'. Both disorders are characterised by an extreme fear of being fat.

Aren't anorexics just young women who have become obsessed with dieting?
People with anorexia certainly become obsessed with dieting, but the condition makes them so afraid of becoming fat that it rules their lives and compels them to lose weight in a manner which goes far beyond the dictates of fashion. Part of the problem is that sufferers often believe there is nothing wrong with losing weight in the way that they do and do not accept help.

They often become very depressed and the weight loss can seriously damage and endanger their health. Although anorexia nervosa is most common amongst young women, it can also affect young children, boys and young men.

Personality disorders

Personality disorders are deeply ingrained patterns of behaviour which are inconsistent and inflexible responses to a broad range of personal and social situations. They may be associated with distress and problems in social functioning. There are several types of personality disorder. For example, some people are so shy or dependent that they find it distressing and difficult to make friends.

• The above is an extract from *Mental Illness – What does it mean?*, produced by the Department of Health.

© Department of Health
March, 1996

Mental health and the young

Emotional and mental health problems in the young: the facts

Two million children and young people suffer from mental distress. Problems tend to become more apparent in older children. Young adolescents (aged 14-15) are three times more likely to have emotional and conduct disorders than children aged 10-11 years.

It is often difficult to correctly identify the problems. Studies show that 23% of children attending GP surgeries (2 million) have some form of psychological or emotional problem, but only 2% are identified by GPs (173,000). Even in paediatric outpatients clinics, only 1 in 3 cases is identified.

Most problems are relatively mild and temporary, perhaps brought on by particular life events such as a change of school. However, 250,000 children under the age of 16 in the UK (2%) are affected by problems which need specialist help. Approximately 10,000 suffer from psychotic illness (which affects the ability to distinguish between reality and imagination), usually following the onset of puberty.

Special services for children and young people in distress are inadequate and children and young people are increasingly having to be treated in adult units. The Department of Health has stated that between 1985 and 1990, the number of NHS psychiatric admissions of those aged between 10 and 14 rose from 145 to 176 per 100,000. Admissions of under-10s rose by 42% and of 15- to 19-year-olds by 21%. By comparison, adult admissions fell 9%, to 2,692 per 100,000.

Statistics quoted are from *Mental Illness: The Fundamental Facts*, published by the Mental Health Foundation.

What sort of problems do children and young people experience?

Common psychological and emotional problems include eating disorders such as anorexia or bulimia, sleep difficulties, aggression, subdued behaviour and failure to thrive. Small children may stop talking after seeing language as a weapon or a source of unhappiness at home, or because they don't get a proper response from their parents when they do talk. Older children may suddenly stop learning at school or be unable to make friends and find themselves isolated and lonely.

Depression

Just like adults, children and young people get depressed, but they are more likely to talk about feeling miserable, fed-up or bored. Sometimes they may say that they wish they were dead. Young adolescents often feel miserable, but when they get depressed they may become withdrawn and stay in their room. Depression may affect their performance at school. Alternatively, they may become angry or cry, or say that they are no good. They may start to misuse alcohol or drugs.

Anxiety

Anxiety in childhood and adolescence can be general or be focused upon a particular thing and become a fear. In both cases the anxiety or fear may be justifiable or illogical. Small children may cling excessively when anxious, insecure, miserable or preoccupied. Older children may appear wary or tense, have problems with sleeping, flinch very easily when startled and be constantly asking for reassurance.

School phobia

Some children develop a powerful fear of attending school and find themselves unable to leave home and go to school. This often becomes an issue after a child has been off school with an illness.

Obsessions

These are anxious, repetitive thoughts that crowd unwelcomed into the mind and are difficult to get rid of. Often they give rise to compulsive rituals such as counting, hand-washing or cleaning which are intended to ward off such thoughts or deal with the anxieties that they produce. These obsessional rituals are unpleasant and severe, much more distressing than the simple rituals that children put into their games.

Why do they have these problems?

Problems can arise in the family, in school or through friends and activities away from home. Young children are more likely to become anxious for reasons to do with their family. With older children and teenagers, factors outside the home, such as problems with authorities, become increasingly important.

The risk of childhood mental health problems increases in families under stress, perhaps because parents are unemployed, living alone or homeless, where a parent suffers from mental illness or when child abuse occurs. Many children who run away from home do so because of physical or sexual abuse and this may lead to mental distress. Problems within the family include rows between parents, parental illness, parents using excessive threats to control their children and parents who over-expose children to adult worries (sex, money, unemployment). Conversely, excessive secrecy and failure to communicate openly with children can also cause distress.

Areas of difficulty at school include trouble with other children (bullying, rejection and teasing), trouble with work (grades and exam results) and trouble with teachers.

Young people may also get anxious concerning physical appearance, girl- and boy-friends or trouble with authorities such as the police.

Where can parents/carers get help?

It is important that parents and carers who are worried about the mental health of children or young people seek advice early, before problems become established. Firstly, they should approach their family doctor, who will help directly or refer them to a specialist if necessary. Health visitors and schools offer advice on how to care for children whose behaviour is difficult to manage, and educational psychologists can offer professional help on school-related problems. The local specialist Child and Family Service, sometimes known as Child Guidance or The Child and Adolescent Centre, can also be contacted through the local health authority.

• The Mental Health Foundation supports research and innovative community project working with children and young people with mental health problems. For further information, please contact the Information Office, 37 Mortimer St, London W1N 8JU. Tel: 0171-580-0145   © *The Mental Health Foundation*

Help! I'm losing control

October 10 is World Mental Health Day, a campaign to challenge the mad stereotypes about mental health. *Just 17* **gets the lowdown on feeling low . . .**

You may not realise it, but mental illness is as common as heart disease, and three times as common as cancer. In fact, one in seven of us will experience a mental health problem during our lives – whether it's minor anxiety or depression or a much rarer disorder like schizophrenia.

Teenagers can be particularly vulnerable, what with the pressure of exams, bullying, first-time sex, self-esteem crises and family hassles. But there's nothing to be ashamed of. After all, we're only human – just like these three *J17* readers who tell us how they coped when they were pushed to the brink . . .

Stella, 15, hurt herself to escape her inner pain . . .

'When I was 14, my parents were splitting up and my life was very stressful. The first time I cut myself, I'd just dumped my boyfriend for cheating on me and I was furious. I don't know why, but I picked up a knife and slashed my arm with it. I remember watching it bleed, while all the tension flooded out of my body. I didn't feel pain, just relief.

Afterwards, I hid the scar under my jumper sleeve.

'The next time was after a huge argument with my mum. Again I used a knife, but this time I attacked my right thigh. The physical sensation distracted me from my emotions and I felt loads better afterwards.

'I continued to cut myself on and off for a year and a half, usually on my own in my bedroom, using my art scalpels. Sometimes I'd just punch the wall, but usually I'd carve up my arm. Whenever anything got on top of me. I'd let it out through bleeding.

House of pain

'I knew it was dangerous and looked ugly, but I just kept doing it and no one even suspected. I've always had trouble getting rid of anger, so cutting myself seemed to be the only way to make the bad feelings go away.

'A few months ago, I had one of those days where everything goes wrong and I couldn't take it. I was sitting on a park bench alone, when I picked up a broken bottle and mutilated my hand really badly. Blood was pouring out, but instead of feeling happy, I just felt numb.

Everybody hurts

'That night my friend noticed my cuts and asked what had happened. Because I was caught off-guard I blurted out the whole story. She gave me a hug and said she was always there for me. Since then, I've started talking about my problems and writing down how I feel in my diary. I find that works much better than reaching for a knife.'

Julie, 16, hated herself so much she wanted to die . . .

'I first got depressed about three years ago. All my friends had boyfriends while no lad had ever shown any interest in me. I thought I was fat and ugly, and I was convinced I'd always be alone.

'I'd lie on my bed crying and thinking, "I hate myself. I've got nothing to look forward to. What's the point of living any more?" I knew I was becoming withdrawn and miserable, but I couldn't break out of it. At school I was getting picked on too 'cause I was shy and didn't hang out with the trendy crowd.

To die for

'After about a year, I'd had enough and wanted to kill myself. I remember listening to my mum planning a visit to my grandparents the next weekend and thinking, "I'll be dead by then." I wrote suicide notes and planned to suffocate myself, but when I lay down on my bed and pressed a pillow over my face, I could still breathe. I tried using a carrier bag instead, but that didn't work either. I gave up in tears, feeling stupid 'cause I couldn't even kill myself properly.

On my own

'A couple of weeks later, Mum noticed I was losing weight and took me to my GP. The doctor advised me to talk to a therapist, but I refused to go. At that point I just had a wall around me that people couldn't get through. I was ashamed of my unhappiness and didn't want to burden my family with any of my problems.

Desperate measures

'After that I convinced myself that I was fine, but at the end of last year I started having fits of depression again. I was stressed by doing my GCSEs and everything just got on top of me. So one day I went into the garage, planning to gas myself with the car exhaust. It was terrifying and I suddenly thought, "I just can't do this."

'That was the turning point for me. Afterwards I threw myself into making new friends. Getting out of the house more helped too, and whenever I felt bad, I'd try to think positive thoughts instead. It wasn't easy, but I was determined to get better. Of course, there's always the chance that my depression may come back, but I don't ever intend to feel that miserable or alone ever again.'

When Take That split up, Annie, 16, needed therapy to control her grief . . .

'I was a massive Take That fan for four years, and it was like belonging to a family. There was always something to do, whether it was watching them on TV, organising gig tickets or visiting the lads' houses. Sometimes I'd get upset 'cause I couldn't be with them, and Mum used to say, "They bring you more depression than happiness." I thought they'd never do anything to hurt me, though. But then all of a sudden they did.

'Last February when the split was announced, I became an emotional wreck. When I watched their final press conference on telly, I was shaking and had a panic-induced asthma attack. I felt both angry and upset that they were abandoning me.

Never forget

'Afterwards I sat in my room crying and became lost in a deep depression. I couldn't see the point in going on, and I didn't want to talk to any of my friends about it or go out. I stopped eating and became really lethargic.

'When I'd had problems before, Take That had always been there for me, but now my whole base had been torn away. I'd gone from being happy and outgoing to introverted and depressed. I just couldn't pull myself together.

Everything changes

'After about three weeks, my parents arranged for me to see a counsellor. I didn't want to go, 'cause I thought no one could possibly understand how I felt about Take That. But the counsellor made me realise that it was OK to feel the way I did, and that I wasn't alone. She said it was just like the feelings bereaved people have – first disbelief, then anger, grief, followed by gradual acceptance.

'The split was like a death for me. Take That had been the most important part of my life for years and all of a sudden they were gone. But gradually I was able to enjoy the

---

I was stressed by doing my GCSEs and everything just got on top of me. So one day I went into the garage, planning to gas myself with the car exhaust. It was terrifying and I suddenly thought, 'I just can't do this.'

---

memories without getting so upset. I still get down, but now I look at the situation more positively and try to get on with my life.'

J17 investigates

Advice

When you're feeling as if there's no hope, keep the following points in mind:

- Asking for help, from a friend or trained counsellor, is not a sign of weakness but of strength.

- Don't bottle up your feelings. Talk to someone you trust.

- Sometimes it's hard to tell the difference between feeling blue and deep depression. If you can't shake your sadness, seek help.

- Identify the cause of your unhappiness. Bullying, exam stress, divorce, a death in the family or getting dumped by your boyfriend can all cause you grief.

- Problems with drinks, drugs, eating or sex are often attempts to escape deeper worries. Counselling helps you confront the cause as well as the symptoms.

- Suicide will destroy your family and friends – not to mention your one, precious shot at life.

If you're depressed, these helplines can offer support:

- MIND Infoline on 0345 66163 can refer you on to a mental-health specialist in your area.
- Careline on 0181-514 1177 offers confidential counselling. Calls are charged at the local rate.
- ChildLine on 0800 1111. Free confidential counselling, 24 hours.
- Samaritans on 0345 909090. Confidential counselling, 24 hours.
- The Anti-Bullying Campaign on 0171-378 1446 gives advice and help on all aspects of bullying.
- Bristol Crisis Service for Women on 0117 925119 (Fri and Sat 9pm – 12.30am). A helpline for women who harm themselves.

Mental health problems – what do they mean?

A lot of people find it hard to cope at times. This may be because a friend or relative has died; there may be job worries or money problems; friendships or relationships may have ended unhappily.

Mental health problems – what do they mean?

When things like this happen, many people naturally feel sad or depressed, alone or angry. Sometimes they may show how they feel by being rude or grumpy, or by wanting to be alone a lot, or to go out all the time. These are usually ordinary reactions to uncomfortable feelings and upsetting events in life which we all may experience. However, some people's reactions may become more disturbing. If, for example, (1) your mother or father refuses to leave her or his room for a long period of time, is unable to make the effort to get washed and dressed, and maybe shouts angrily for most of the day; or (2) if your brother or sister thinks that voices are telling him or her what to do and is bewildered and afraid, then it could be that he or she is suffering from a serious mental health problem.

They may, in other words, become extremely confused, agitated or withdrawn; and they may find it difficult to tell the difference between what they are imagining and what is actually happening. There are different kinds of serious mental-health problems, two of the most common are manic depression and schizophrenia.

Here are some types of mental illness:

Manic-depressive illness causes extreme changes in mood, from high spirits and over-activity to deep depression and lethargy; it often causes irritability that can be very wearing for the family. When someone is overly excited he or she may spend all their money on, say, expensive presents, so that there is nothing left for the rent or clothes or food. When that person is feeling low and depressed, he or she may cry a lot, want to sleep all the time, or just stay in bed and be incapable of looking after the family and the household, and carrying on with their usual work.

Schizophrenia causes a great deal of distress and confusion in people's minds. It can lead to a person hearing voices, telling him or her what to do and producing strong feelings of confusion, bewilderment and fear; and it can cause him or her to think that all his or her thoughts and actions are being controlled by others. Sometimes people with schizophrenia are convinced that the television is sending messages to them, or that neighbours are always talking about them, watching them or planning to hurt them. Because these strange ideas seem so real, they might throw the TV out of the window or shout at the neighbours or make complaints to the police. It is very hard for them to tell the difference between what is real and what is not real. At times they can lose interest in life completely, finding it hard to talk or show affection and not bothering to eat or to dress properly, or to keep warm. Most people with these kind of serious mental-health problems can be helped with treatment and support in special day centres or hospitals. They can find new ways of managing and carrying on their normal lives.

There are other types of mental illness, for example, *dementia* in old people, when some grandparents may become very forgetful and confused, and their behaviour becomes unpredictable. Some people suffer from *obsessive compulsive disorder* when, for example, they may feel that they have to keep things extremely clean and tidy or they become very anxious. Some sufferers may try to persuade everyone else to help with their rituals of cleaning.

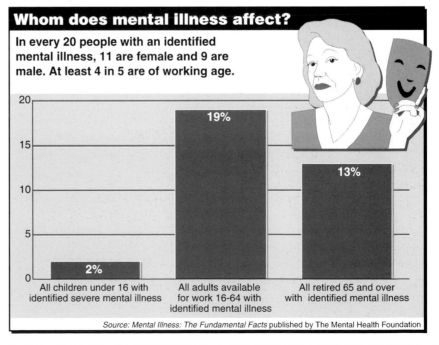

Whom does mental illness affect?

In every 20 people with an identified mental illness, 11 are female and 9 are male. At least 4 in 5 are of working age.

All children under 16 with identified severe mental illness	2%
All adults available for work 16-64 with identified mental illness	19%
All retired 65 and over with identified mental illness	13%

Source: Mental Illness: The Fundamental Facts published by The Mental Health Foundation

How does this make you feel?

If your mum or dad or favourite aunt or uncle has become, during this time, a very different person, it may seem that no one is there to look after you, to listen to your worries or problems, or to help you with your feelings, too. You may feel scared, unsure and angry, sad or lonely. You may be ashamed or embarrassed and not understand what is happening. Maybe you don't want anyone else to know, you may even have worries about your own mental health – that you have, or will have, the same problem as your mum or dad. You may even feel angry with them for making you feel so frightened and confused.

It will always help to talk to someone else, and to find an adult who can understand. Can you go to a friend's parent, your teacher, school nurse or youth leader – someone you think will listen to you? They may be able to reassure you and help you to get the right support from a doctor or a social worker. Try not to stay alone and frightened or worried. Your support, love and understanding can be of great value, it may mean a great deal to your mum or dad, or other family member, to know you care about him or her even though sometimes you may feel fed up with them and wish they could do better. But remember, it is not your responsibility to make them well – there is a limit to how far you yourself can help them. Most people who suffer from periods of mental illness need professional help, arranged through their GP, and they can improve with therapy and medication.

Where to go/ask for help

Your GP, teacher, a family friend you can confide in, or a social worker, school nurse, youth worker at your local youth centre, club or church/temple, or volunteer bureau. Organisations which can offer help, support, information or advice include:

- Childline, 2nd Floor, Royal Mail Building, Studd Street, London N1 0QW or Freepost 1111 London N1 0BR Tel: 0800 1111
- The Manic Depression Fellowship, 10 High Street, Kingston upon Thames, Surrey KT1 1EY Tel: 0181 974 6550. This is the Head Office, they may be able to put you in touch with a local support group for your parent.
- National Schizophrenia Fellowship, 28 Castle Street, Kingston upon Thames, Surrey KT1 1SS. Tel: 0181 547 3937 / Advice line 0181 974 6814 (10am-3pm weekdays) NSF has local groups including Sib-Link groups for brothers and sisters of people suffering from schizophrenia.
- Network: a voice for young carers, PO Box 558, London SW2 2EL. They produce a newsletter for young carers.
- Samaritans. Call 0345 909090 for your local branch. 24-hour service for people who want to talk about any problem, not only suicide.
- Saneline. Tel: 0345 678000 Helpline open from 2pm until midnight every day of the year. They have information on mental illness and details of local support.
- Youth Access, Ashby House, Ashby Road, Loughborough, Leicester LE11 3AE Tel: 01509 210420. This organisation has a network of informal, confidential youth counselling and information centres all over the UK.
- Young Carers (Part of the Carers National Association), 20-25 Glasshouse Yard, London EC1A 4JS Tel: Carersline 0171 490 8898. Produce a Young Carers Information Pack, free to young carers.
- Young Carers Research Group, Loughborough University, Leicester LE11 3TU Tel: 01509 228299. Publish a national directory of Young Carers Projects and Initiatives. Tel: 01509 228299 (publications) / 01509 223379 (information).

© Young Minds

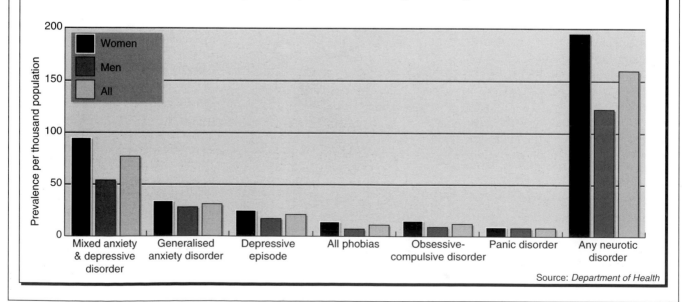

Weekly prevalence of neurotic disorders by sex

About one in six adults, aged 16 to 64, in Great Britain suffered a neurotic disorder in the week before interview. The most prevalent neurotic disorder was mixed anxiety and depressive disorder (77 cases per thousand). For all six neurotic disorders the prevalence was higher among women than men.

Source: *Department of Health*

Hidden signs of a depressed child

Two in every 100 children need psychiatric help, yet spotting the symptoms can defeat even an expert, says Christine Doyle

This week, the parliamentary committee inquiring into children's health starts taking evidence on what can be done to combat child depression. Recent research has shown that in reasonably stable social circumstances, as many as two in 100 under-12s are so depressed that they would benefit from psychiatric help.

According to figures in *So Young, So Sad, So Listen* – a publication for parents and teachers produced by the Royal College of Psychiatrists and the West London Health Promotion Agency – another four or five in every 100 show signs of significant distress.

The incidence of depression increases with age and is related to the amount of community support available: in troubled inner-city areas, child depression rates double. The problem is compounded by mothers whose depression often stems directly from their circumstances.

Although the condition is prevalent, it often seems hidden because many young people do not have the words to express how they feel.

Children tend to become depressed as a result of a particular experience or set of circumstances. These include: suffering physical, sexual or verbal abuse; having rowing or divorcing parents; living in a hostile or isolated environment; the family being under extreme financial pressure; or the child or some other family member suffering chronic illness or disability. Because a number of these factors affect many generations of the same family, depression often tends to be handed down.

Spotting a depressed child is not always easy. While some are sad and withdrawn, others manifest their disturbed mental state by being exhibitionist and aggressive.

Sue Jenner, a child clinical psychologist, says: 'Such children often lose their self-esteem. I treated one child who drew beautifully, but who would destroy his efforts when he was praised. One nine-year-old girl, with above-average intelligence, fell behind in class. Eventually, she told her teacher that she was interested and wanted to work, but felt "too sad" to apply herself. The trouble is that many teachers are too busy coping with the rest of the class to pick up on these signs.'

Other danger signals are eating

'Crisis out of a drama' on unstable children

By Natalie Clarke

Mental health experts were accused of 'sales talk' yesterday after claiming that thousands of children are unstable and need professional help.

The British Psychological Society, which has given evidence to MPs on the health select committee inquiry into children's health, said one child in four suffers mental problems.

It called for more specialist treatment for such youngsters, claiming only 20 to 33 per cent receive the help they need.

Psychosis, eating problems, disruptive behaviour and suicidal tendencies are among the more severe mental disorders suffered by the nation's children, says child psychiatrist Dr Richard Williams who co-ordinated the society's study.

He warned that 'latchkey children' and those who were fostered from family to family were particularly at risk.

Dr Williams, former director of the Health Advisory Service, said it was 'imperative' that children at risk of mental problems were identified.

Jan Hildreth, a governor at the public school Wellington College, dismissed the society's claims last night.

'These are sensational figures,' he said. 'I think children will love this because it means they'll have lots of attention paid to them.

'I'd have thought saying, "Don't be silly and get on with your work" would be more effective.' He added: 'We have a psychiatrist here who meets the headmaster and offers advice on pupils. But that is very different. This sounds like a bit of sales talk by the psychologists.'

Professor Brice Pitt of the Royal College of Psychiatrists said professional help was not the solution. 'I suspect that anything that moved us back to the traditional family structure might be rewarded by less disturbance.'

© The Daily Mail
December, 1996

problems, chronic fatigue and – in teenagers – abuse of drink or drugs. Children as young as five can become suicidally depressed: one five-year-old suffocated herself by placing a plastic bag over her head; others, says Jenner, 'linger by motorways, or have a fascination for bottles containing poisonous substances.'

Peter Hall, founder of the Royal Shakespeare Company, was a sufferer. In his autobiography, he describes his 'suicidal depression' at the age of eight.

About six in every 100,000 boys and two in every 100,000 girls aged 15-19 commit suicide. Significantly, parents often have no idea that their teenager is harbouring suicidal thoughts.

Jenner thinks helping parents to understand what is going on is vital: 'Many parents with depressed children are not likely to be on any social worker hit list. But often they are not speaking to their children in what I call a child-centred way.

'These parents tend to be directive and prescriptive and give many commands or ask lots of questions. Often this is done in a critical or undermining way, such as, "Who's a clever boy then?"

> **Children as young as five can become suicidally depressed: one five-year-old suffocated herself by placing a plastic bag over her head**

accompanied by a sneer. Children require discipline and commands, but balance is crucial – praise, smiles and

the inclusion of parents in what they are doing is essential.'

Jenner encourages such parents. 'It is never too late to change. Often parents do not realise the child feels deprived of love and attention. Sometimes, a child's behaviour can change dramatically after just one or two sessions with a parent behaving differently.'

As a rough guide, help should be sought when a child's depression has not lifted after two to three weeks and there is clear interference with his or her daily life.

© Telegraph Group Limited, London 1996

That old shrinking feeling

Just what is a psychoanalyst? Sally Weintrobe explains the shift in perspective since the early days for both patient and practitioner

At present anyone can call him or herself a psychoanalyst and, judging by what is written in the newspapers, frequently does. So who and what is a psychoanalyst?

Mental health professionals in this country generally accept that a psychoanalyst is someone who has been clinically trained by the Institute of Psycho-Analysis, the training body of the British Psychoanalytical Society. Psychoanalysts are in the tradition pioneered by Freud. Modern-day Jungians call

themselves analytical psychologists or Jungian analysts.

Psychoanalytic ideas have had

> **The psychoanalyst has become an icon – usually as a man, although just as likely these days to be a woman – of popular culture**

a huge influence on the way many psychotherapists work. Sometimes the influence is a loose one; sometimes, as in the case of psycho-analytically-oriented psycho-therapists whose training is centrally based on ideas and methods from clinical psychoanalysis, the influence is more formal.

The psychoanalyst has become an icon – usually as a man, although just as likely these days to be a woman – of popular culture. The public has its own relationship with what the psychoanalyst is, quite separate from how the profession sees and defines itself. One place their relationship shows is in cartoons and jokes. Through humour we can focus and defuse our fear of finding ourselves in the vulnerable position of needing help with emotional problems and putting our trust in another person. In the world of the joke, the doctor is bound to let us die, the lawyer will certainly fleece us and the psychoanalyst, along with the psychiatrist, will be a head shrinker.

'Shrinker' is an old word meaning someone who disavows the truth or diminishes the stature of a person. Jokes about shrinks can be revealing of people's ambivalence about gaining self-knowledge and looking at the truth about themselves. People tend to disown thoughts and feelings when they cause too much conflict or distress. 'It's not we who are out of touch! It's the shrink!' We can locate in the psychoanalyst what we don't like to see in ourselves. We send her up and send her on her way.

What does the psychoanalyst look at in her work with the patient? By studying the particular ways in which the patient interacts with her in the relationship he forms with her, she hopes to gain an understanding of the difficulties that have brought him to analysis.

How has psychoanalysis evolved and changed since Freud? I think the biggest change that has taken place within psychoanalysis is one that was largely pioneered by British psychoanalysts. In earlier days the psychoanalyst tended to see her own inner responses to the patient primarily as a

source of bias. She now recognises her inner responses as an important source of data, potentially very helpful to her in her attempts to understand the patient's underlying thoughts and feelings. Paradoxically, the more the psychoanalyst realises she is an inevitable part of what she studies, the better chance she has to think clearly about what might belong to the patient.

. . . the psychoanalyst aims to try to help the patient with his problems by working with him in a disciplined, thoughtful way

---

I think this shift in perspective has influenced the way the psychoanalyst writes about her work. Of course what she says is bounded by confidentiality and this very much restricts the information she is able to give. How the psychoanalyst thinks about the patient and how she conveys the experience of being with the patient tend nowadays to be described in a way that is more easily understandable to the public. There is less abstract theory and more description of a relationship.

This is reassuring because the reader is in a better position to have a view of how the psychoanalyst thinks about the patient and is more able to agree, to disagree and to consult his or her own intuitive knowledge of people and common sense about what the psychoanalyst is saying.

Because she is part of what she studies, it is important that the psychoanalyst takes very seriously the ongoing possibility that her inner reactions may stem from her own limitations and conflicts. There is always a potential for people to study the problems of others as a means of avoiding looking at their own problems. For this reason a basic requirement to be a psychoanalyst is to undergo a thorough personal psychoanalysis and this is an obligatory part of the training.

In her work the psychoanalyst questions herself carefully about what she thinks she understands about the patient. She knows that what she thinks may not be right and she also knows that, if the patient agrees with what she says, this may be because the patient is being compliant. Psychoanalysis is a discipline and the psychoanalyst aims to try to help the patient with his problems by working with him in a disciplined, thoughtful way.

All psychoanalysts are listed in the register of the British Confederation of Psychotherapists. Information about the register can be obtained by telephoning the BCP at 0181-830-5173.

The Institute of Psychoanalysis (tel: 0171-580-4952) trains psychoanalysts and runs a clinic (tel: 0171-436-1177) where patients can apply to have psychoanalysis at a reduced fee.

Suicidal behaviour in children and young people

How common is suicidal behaviour?

Suicide is likely to be underreported for all age groups. This is particularly true for young people, partly because coroners and others can be reluctant to return a suicide verdict for young people below their mid-teens. Statistics are likely to be more reliable from around 15 years.

The most recent available mortality statistics for England and Wales relate to 1994.[3] These indicate that five boys and two girls aged between ten and 14 years (representing 0.3 and 0.1 per 100,000 population), as well as 65 males and 12 females in the 15 to 19 years age group (4.2 and 0.8 per 100,000 respectively), died as a result of suicide and self-inflicted injury. A further eight males and seven females in the younger, and 64 males and 14 females in the older, group died following injuries which were undetermined as to whether they were accidentally or purposely inflicted.

Parasuicide is far more common than completed suicide and, by contrast, occurs between two and three times as often among young females as males. Statistics are not routinely collected, but it has been suggested that around 19,000 young people between ten and 19 years are likely to be referred annually to general hospitals in England and Wales following self-poisoning or self-injury. Some 2,000 of these are between ten and 14 years, and the vast majority are girls.[2]

It is impossible to know how often young people have suicidal thoughts, and estimates – which suggest that up to one in two young people think about killing themselves on occasion – depend considerably on study samples and methodologies.

By Dr Nicola Madge

Methods of suicide and parasuicide

The most usual method of parasuicide in adolescence is poisoning, often by a drug overdose.[1,4] Hanging, jumping, drowning, shooting, drug overdosing and inhalation of car exhaust fumes are the usual means of completed suicide. There are some sex differences in that males tend to use more aggressive methods (particularly hanging) while females favour overdosing, commonly with paracetamol.

Recent trends

There has been much concern about rapidly rising suicide rates among young men – but not young women – in the United Kingdom,[5] and it has been pointed out that rates in England and Wales increased by 78 per cent among those aged 15 to 24 between 1980 and 1990.

The number of cases of recorded suicide among children and young people between ten and 20 years has, however, not risen so dramatically over this period and indeed has shown considerable fluctuation. There appears to have been a decline in such deaths for ten- to 14-year-olds – although numbers were up considerably in both 1993 and 1994.[3] By contrast, lower rates were reported for 15- to 19-year-olds in 1993 and 1994 than for any other year since 1980.

Trends in attempted suicide among young people are unclear, although some suggestion of a current increase, mostly among girls, has emerged from a recent Oxford study.[4]

Gender differences

Particularly striking, but puzzling, are the differing patterns of suicidal behaviour among young males and females. While statistics show, for almost all dates and in most countries, that young males complete suicide more often than young females and

Reported suicide

Suicide is likely to be underreported for all age groups. This is particularly true for young people, partly because coroners and others can be reluctant to return a suicide verdict for young people below their mid-teens. Statistics are likely to be more reliable from around 15 years.

Numbers and rates per 100,000 in brackets.

	Males 10-14 yrs	Males 15-19 yrs	Females 10-14 yrs	Females 15-19 yrs
England & Wales 1994 [source: Office of National Statistics, London]	5 (0.3)	65 (4.2)	2 (0.1)	12 (0.8)
Finland 1995 [source: Statistics Finland]	4 (2.4)	42 (25.1)	–	6 (3.7)
Germany, West 1994 [source: Statistisches Bundesamt, Wiesbaden]	22 (1.3)	173 (10.2)	13 (0.8)	47 (2..9)
Ireland (Republic) 1995 [source: Central Statistics Office, Cork]	2 (1.2)	30 (17.9)	1 (0.6)	5 (3.1)
Norway 1994 [source: Statistics, Norway]	6 (4.4)	26 (18.5)	2 (1.6)	6 (4.5)

are alone responsible for recent upward trends,[1] it remains true that the vast majority of individuals involved in deliberate self-harm are female.[4]

Many commentators highlight the need for research into the reasons for these differences. Do males and females face different amounts, and/or types of stress, do they react negatively to different stresses, or do similar stresses affect them in dissimilar ways?

International differences

There are also indications of variations between individual countries in the rates of, and trends in, children and young people recorded as dying from suicide. National statistics[6] suggest, for example, that more such deaths occur in Norway and Hungary than in Italy and Britain – although, as already noted, some differences may be attributable to recording procedures. Furthermore, national statistics indicate that whereas rates have been increasing over recent years in Ireland, Italy and Norway, they have been much more stable in England and Wales, and are actually decreasing in Germany and Hungary.

Marked international differences are, in addition, found for parasuicide. A recent European multi-centre study has shown that rates for 15- to 24-year-old males between 1989 and 1992 were particularly high in Helsinki in Finland, Cergy-Pontoise in France, and Oxford in England, but relatively low in the Italian and Spanish study centres.[7]

Who is at risk?

Young people who commit suicide rarely leave notes to explain their actions, they cannot be interviewed after the event, and the memories of surviving family and friends are likely to be affected by the adolescent's death and hence unreliable. Moreover, limited insight can be gained from talking to other young people who have merely thought about suicide or made a 'failed' attempt.

Overall, and partly because of the small numbers involved, little headway has been made over the past 25 years in the prediction of suicide.[8] There is, nonetheless, a need to try to understand the reasons for adolescent suicide, and psychological autopsy studies, despite their inevitable limitations, often provide the best clues. These studies involve collecting and analysing (often by independent psychiatrists) any available data from relatives, friends and acquaintances, professional workers and official records.

The best evidence suggests that risk factors include both personal characteristics and situational variables. Often a combination of circumstances, perhaps triggered by a final rejection of some kind, provides the best possible explanation in individual cases.

The role of depression

Depression is thought to be a particularly significant risk factor for suicidal behaviour. Studies in New York[9] and Finland[10] have suggested that over 90 per cent of child and adolescent suicides have a long-standing psychiatric disorder. According to Shaffer,[11] girls who commit suicide tend to be depressed or under temporary stress whereas boys are more likely to have a history of aggressive behaviour, often coupled with alcohol or drug abuse. All the same, most depressed adolescents do not demonstrate suicidal behaviour and many of those that do are not suffering from diagnosable depressive disorders.

Stressful experiences

Various negative stress experiences have been linked with suicidal behaviour although none on its own can be considered a 'high risk' factor.[1,10] Early background circumstances including parental loss, family disruption, deprivation and poverty, on the one hand, and more contemporary events such as school pressures, problems with parents or boy/girl friends, physical and sexual abuse, or witnessing a suicide at first hand or in the media have, on the other, been suggested. Suicidal behaviour in adolescents may reflect unsuccessful strategies for coping with stress.

References

1 Diekstra, RFW, Kienhorst, CWM and de Wilde, E J (1995) 'Suicide and suicidal behaviour among adolescents' in Rutter, M and Smith, DJ (eds) *Psychosocial Disorders in Young People: Time trends and their causes*. Wiley

2 Hawton, K and Fagg, J (1992) 'Deliberate self-poisoning and self-injury in adolescents. A study of characteristics and trends in Oxford, 1976-89', *British Journal of Psychiatry*, 161, 816-23

3 Office of Population Censuses and Surveys (1995) 'Deaths in 1994 by cause.' *OPCS Monitor* DH2 95/1

4 Hawton, K, Fagg, J and Simkins, S (1996) 'Deliberate self-poisoning and self-injury in children and adolescents under 16 years of age in Oxford, 1976-1993', *British Journal of Psychiatry*, 169, 741-7

5 Hawton, K (1992) 'By their own young hand', *British Medical Journal*, 304, 6833, 1000

6 Available from national statistic offices in the countries specified

7 Schmidtke, A and others (1994) 'Rates and trends of attempted suicide in Europe, 1989-1992' in Kerkhof, AJFM and others (eds) *Attempted Suicide in Europe. Findings from the multicentre study on parasuicide by the WHO Regional Office for Europe*. Leiden: DSWO Press

8 Van Egmond, M and Diekstra, R (1990) 'The predictability of suicidal behaviour: the results of a meta-analysis of published studies', *Crisis*, 11, 2, 57-84

9 Shaffer, D, Gould, M and Hicks, R (1994) 'Epidemiology, mechanisms and clinical features of youth suicide' in Kelleher, MJ (ed.) *Divergent Perspectives on Suicidal Behaviour*. Cork: Fifth European Symposium on Suicide

10 Marttunen, M and others (1992) 'Adolescent suicide: end-point of long-term difficulties', *Journal of the American Academy of Child and Adolescent Psychiatry*, 31, 649-54

11 Shaffer, D (1988) 'The epidemiology of teen suicide: an examination of risk factors', *Journal of Clinical Psychiatry Supplement*, 9, 49, 35-41

- The above is an extract from *Suicidal behaviour in children and young people*, Highlight No. 144, published by National Children's Bureau. See page 39 for address details.

Understanding depression

Information from MIND

What depression is

There must be few people who always feel good about themselves and are completely satisfied with their lives. Most people like themselves in some ways and not others, and like some aspects of their lives but not others. They may sometimes go through bad patches but do not think of themselves as having mental health problems. For others life is more of a struggle. They feel bad about themselves and their lives in most ways. At times they feel complete despair. It is this last group who can be said to be depressed.

These are some of the things you may experience if you are depressed:
- Disliking or even hating yourself.
- Disliking or hating people in general.
- Being preoccupied with negative thoughts and seeing the worst in everything.
- Rather than feeling alive with anger or grief you are more likely to feel numb, empty and despondent.
- Blaming yourself and feeling unnecessarily guilty about things.
- Finding it is an effort to do the simplest tasks. This can include difficulties with concentration and making decisions, even about the smallest things. You may also be unusually irritable and impatient.
- Your sleep pattern is likely to change. You may wake up early in the mornings and not be able to go back to sleep or you may sleep for longer than usual.
- Similarly with eating. You may stuff yourself with food and put on weight, or not bother to eat properly and lose weight.
- Using more tobacco, alcohol or other drugs than usual.

- Cutting yourself off from others rather than asking for help.

In its mildest form depression does not stop you from leading your normal life, but it makes everything harder to do and seem less worthwhile.

At its most severe it is life-threatening. You may feel like killing yourself or simply give up trying to live. In very rare cases people who are extremely depressed may even want to kill those they care about to spare them from having to live in this world.

People who are depressed are often also anxious. You become anxious when you feel threatened, whether the threat is real or something you imagine. Physical symptoms of anxiety include headaches, aching muscles, sweating and dizziness. The mind of someone who is anxious is usually full of busy, repetitive thoughts. It can then be hard to concentrate, or slow down enough to sleep. In the long term anxiety can cause exhaustion and general ill-health. Anxiety is explained more fully in our advice leaflet *Understanding Anxiety*.

Mental health workers sometimes refer to people being clinically depressed. By this they mean that the person is too depressed to help themselves and needs expert assistance. They may also diagnose depression as reactive or endogenous.

Reactive depression is caused by the person's response to external events. Endogenous depression has no obvious external cause. (Endogenous means coming from within.) But this distinction can be misleading.

Post-natal depression is the depression which some mothers experience after their babies are born. A fuller explanation is covered in our advice leaflet *Understanding Post-Natal Depression*.

Manic depression is a condition which causes people to have episodes of depression and of mania. Mania is highly excited and uncontrolled behaviour. Manic depression is explained more fully in our advice leaflet *Understanding Manic Depression*.

Causes of depression

To know what causes depression you have to understand what makes people feel bad about themselves and their lives.

What happened to you when you were a child can have a big effect on how you feel about yourself now. The attitude of parents (or other people who looked after you) is particularly important. Did they tell you they loved you and show it by holding and cuddling you? Did they help you to learn new skills by encouraging rather than criticising you? If not, you are likely to feel bad about yourself. Wider influences are also important: teachers, other children, TV programmes and politicians can all have affected how we feel about ourselves.

How much you like your life obviously depends simply how good it is. But it may also be affected by what you expect. If, for example, you enjoy sports and pride yourself on your fitness, you will be more likely to become depressed by an injury than someone who is not interested

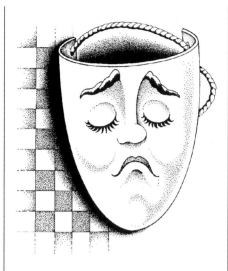

in keeping fit. Changes to your life which involve loss can cause depression: bereavement, divorce, losing your job and so on.

It is possible to overcome the effects of bad experiences in your early life. If, for example, you are well loved now, it may not seem important that you were not when you were young. But you may be vulnerable when things go wrong. Supposing you are married and your husband or wife leaves you. You may respond by deciding it is all your fault and that no one will ever love you again. Then you will not only feel bad about yourself and dislike your life, but feel hopeless about changing it. But someone who was well loved when they were young may respond quite differently; perhaps deciding they deserve someone better anyway.

There are also other causes of depression. It is not just how you feel when something goes wrong that matters; what you do can also affect whether or not you become depressed. Are you the sort of person who responds to bad news by rushing round to see your best friend, throwing your arms around them and bursting into tears? Or do you reach for a drink or a cigarette to dampen down your feelings, tell everyone that you are fine and try to handle it on your own? You are more likely to become and stay depressed if you stop yourself expressing feelings and cut yourself off from people.

Depression can also have physical causes. Physical and mental health are closely linked. Poor diet,

lack of physical fitness and drug abuse can also contribute to depression. People who have had influenza and other illnesses may be depressed for a while after the more obvious symptoms have gone. Changes in the balance of hormones can possibly make it more likely for a woman to become depressed before she has her period, after childbirth or during the menopause. Lack of daylight in the winter months may make people prone to depression. (This is explained in the advice leaflet *Understanding Seasonal Affective Disorder*.) Our genetic make-up may also affect how likely we are to become depressed.

Some illnesses cause symptoms which are similar to those of depression. The patient is sometimes wrongly diagnosed and treated for depression instead of the illness. This has happened to people who have ME (Myalgic Encephalomyelitis).

What you can do

Depression has two important characteristics which you need to be aware of when thinking about what you can do to defeat it:

- It can feed on itself: you get depressed and then you get more depressed about being depressed.
- It can occupy enormous amounts of your time and attention.

Being in a state of depression can then itself become a bigger problem than the difficulties which caused it in the first place. It is important to break the hold the depression has on you. Dwelling on difficulties (unless you are thinking constructively) does not help you to solve them. Try to notice when you are doing it and replace that activity with one of those suggested here:

- Find things to do that are so interesting to you that, at least for a while, you forget that you are depressed.
- Stop being over-concerned with what goes on 'in your head'. Be physical: walk; run; dance; cycle; play a sport.
- Do anything which will make you laugh.

You need to do things which will make you feel better about yourself. Try and treat yourself kindly

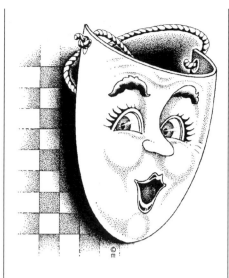

and act as if you do feel good about yourself. If you do that your negative feelings will change. Here are some ideas:

- Look after yourself physically: do not abuse your body with drugs, eat well and get exercise.
- Pay attention to your appearance and the place you live. Try and make them more how you want them to be.
- Try and take a break from your usual routine.

You need to deal with anything that is wrong in your life. Important principles to bear in mind are:

- Ask for help. Other people can listen and help you think things through.
- Act rather than be passive. Do not let fear stop you from making necessary changes.
- Do not sit on your feelings. If you need to cry, cry. If you need to get angry, get angry.

These suggestions may feel as if they are a waste of time or too difficult to take up. But when you are depressed it is best not to be guided by your negative feelings. Do your best to try them anyway and you may be pleased with the results.

You may find that what you can do for yourself, and with the support of your family and friends, is not enough. Help is available from elsewhere.

- The above is an extract from *Understanding Depression*, published by Mind. See page 39 for address details.

Depression in the workplace

The cost of depression

Introduction

Depression is a common illness. Some 20% of women and 10% of men can be expected to suffer from depression at some point during their lives. One in twenty of all adults is estimated to be experiencing depression at any one time. Naturally problems that are common in the general population are common in people at work; the Department of Health and the Confederation of British Industry have estimated that between 15% and 30% of employees will experience some form of mental health problem during their working lives. As well as being a cause of untold distress, depression is linked to poor work performance and high rates of sickness absence, accidents and staff turnover.

What is depression?

People who have not suffered from depression do not know what it is like. Everyone may feel fed up, miserable or sad at certain times, particularly after deeply distressing occasions such as the death of a partner or relative. Usually this kind of sadness passes with time, but occasionally it may drag on or seem to get out of proportion to the unhappy event. Sometimes, un-happiness just comes 'out of the blue', without any obvious reason. Depression that persists, is severe, or that comes to dominate every aspect of the day, is an illness, and those affected will benefit from help.

Certain characteristic symptoms can give a clue that someone is suffering from depression that requires extra help.

These may include:
- Sadness which does not change with circumstances.
- Crying for no apparent reasons.

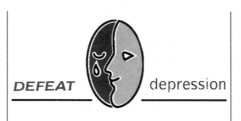

- Anxiety, worrying irritability or tension.
- Disturbed sleep.
- Reduced appetite and loss of weight.
- Tiredness, lethargy and lack of motivation.
- Loss of interest in normal activities.
- Forgetfulness and inability to concentrate.
- Thoughts of worthlessness and hopelessness.

The effects of depression on work

Those suffering from depression will behave uncharacteristically in many aspects of their life – at home and at work. Some features which may become particularly evident to fellow workers or to employers are:
- Slowness and mistakes in work.
- Poor concentration and forget-fulness.
- Poor time-keeping.
- Increase in unexplained absences or sick leave.
- Disputes and arguments with colleagues.

Depression can therefore have far-reaching consequences for the ability of an employee to work effectively. Some of those affected by depression will have to stop work completely for a time because of the severity of their symptoms. Most, however, will attempt to soldier on, painfully aware that they are not performing as well as usual. Recog-nition that an individual is suffering from depression, followed by effective help, will speed his or her return to normal performance at work as well as reducing much needless misery.

Recognition

Colleagues at work are in a good position to notice changes which may suggest that their workmate is suffering from depression and should encourage them to seek help. An early decision to consult the occupational health department, or the family doctor, will allow earlier and more effective treatment. The manager or employer who is aware of an employee's difficulties can be helpful in allowing time off work if the depression is severe, as well as, in due course, encouraging and easing the employee's return to work. Of course, many employees will be afraid of disclosing problems which they fear may affect their job security, so this sensitive issue can often be handled effectively and confi-dentially by the occupational health adviser or the family doctor. Most people will be able to return to work within a few weeks.

Treatment

Talking about feelings is helpful in itself. Many people with depression will start to feel better once they have discussed their problems. The majority of people with depression will be helped more by a variety of treatments which can be provided by doctors or other trained pro-fessionals. Which treatment is most suitable will depend largely upon the individual as well as the nature of the depression. Most treatments fall into two main groups: talking treatments, such as counselling, and anti-depressant tablets, both of which are given as a course of treatment over a period of months.

These can be used singly or together and will speed the recovery from a period of depression. Although there is a common worry that some of the drugs used in the treatment of depression can be addictive, there is in fact no evidence that this is the case. As with most other common illnesses, the majority of people will recover completely from depression and be able, in due course, to return to work as before.

Of great importance in the recovery from depression is the close working together of those providing help, including the family doctor, sometimes a psychiatrist specialising in the treatment of depression and the occupational health adviser who is aware of the demands and conditions of the workplace.

Can unsatisfactory working conditions cause depression?

For most people work provides a structure to the day and the opportunity to make friendships as well as a way of increasing one's sense of self-worth and of feeling valued. For the vast majority of people a steady and rewarding job can be of great benefit in reducing the risk of depression and engendering happiness. It is therefore not surprising that those recently made redundant, or who have been out of work for many months, are at a greater risk of developing depression than those in continuing employment.

Work, therefore, has a largely beneficial impact on mental health, but there are circumstances in which it can be less helpful. Although there is little evidence that poor working conditions can directly cause depressive illness, undue pressure and stress at work can combine with other problems, such as difficulties at home or recent unhappy events, and contribute to the development of depression.

Surveys have shown that certain kinds of work are linked to increased risks of job dissatisfaction and stress. Poor working conditions, such as cramped offices, noisy factories and hot and stuffy shops, may all contribute to stress and tension.

Aspects of the work itself can be important. Jobs in which an employee feels there is little opportunity to use his or her skills, or which are repetitive and inflexible seem particularly likely to result in job dissatisfaction and low morale. Uncertainty about how well a job is done, or about future changes in employment, can result in feelings of tension and worry. 'Difficult' bosses who bully and criticise will worsen any feeling of insecurity in their employees.

Employees who feel they have no say in the way their work is organised or that decisions are imposed from above will be prone to frustration. The introduction of new time-saving computer systems has beneficial effects on the efficiency of an office, but at the same time brings pressing deadlines and demands for quicker decisions, which may produce stress amongst employees. It has also had far-reaching consequences on the way businesses are structured, which can itself affect the people working within them.

So what can be done?

Every company should give consideration to the development of a 'mental health' policy. Such a policy would aim to provide a working environment which is conducive to the prevention of depression and other mental ill health, as well as its prompt and effective treatment. This would be expected to improve the overall performance of the organisation and of individual employees and to reduce costs incurred by sickness absence due to many physical illnesses in addition to those caused by depression.

There are four main areas where such a policy would concentrate:

1. Raising awareness:

Everyone in the company, from the workforce to the senior management, must be made aware of the importance of recognising and helping colleagues who may be suffering from depression. It is also fundamental that everyone understands that positive action can result in very great benefits to both individuals and the company as a whole.

2. Health education for employees:

Employees will benefit from knowledge of mental health issues and instruction in specific techniques for reducing stress. Instruction in time-management and assertiveness training, and the use of 'team-building' exercises may benefit all employees by protecting them from depression and other conditions. Identification of those employees needing assistance can be helped by educating the workforce and management with regard to early recognition of depression, and in what circumstances people become most vulnerable to developing depression. It is particularly important to emphasise the fact that depression is unlikely to permanently affect a person's ability to work.

3. The organisation of the business:

The way in which a business is organised and operated is likely to have an effect on the mental health of its workforce. Important areas include the physical environment at work, the responsibilities inherent in the job and the level of supervision, and selection and training of personnel for particular work. Thoughtful adjustments can enhance the job satisfaction of individual employees and the performance of the business as a whole.

4. Occupational health services:

Occupational Health Departments need to be closely involved with senior management from the earliest stages in the development of programmes to educate line managers and the workforce in the prevention and early recognition of depression. They clearly also have a special role in the recognition, counselling and treatment of depressed employees and in facilitating their return to work. In particular, Occupational Health staff will have experience of sensitive issues such as workplace confidentiality, security of job tenure and the timing of the return to part or full-time working. They are also familiar with the particular stresses and strains of the work environment. Occupational Health nurses and doctors are well placed to work closely with family doctors or other specialist employees, whilst always bearing in mind the importance of issues of confidentiality in the workplace. Contacts should be established with the local branches of various self-help organisations.

© Royal College of Psychiatrists

Not just sticks and stones

A survey of the stigma, taboos and discrimination experienced by people with mental health problems

Main findings

The level of discrimination that this survey, *Not Just Sticks and Stones*, uncovered has shocked many people at Mind, and shows the extent to which stigmas and taboos surrounding mental ill-health affect every area of life including employment, housing, parenting, finances and relationships with family and friends. The findings of this survey raise deep concerns about a large section of the population which is effectively left disenfranchised, and prevented form having a 'stakehold' in society.

A common feeling amongst the vast majority of people was that of being thrown on the scrap-heap as employees, as parents and as valuable members of society just because of their psychiatric histories.

'The level of discrimination revealed by this report is staggering. It confirms our worst fears – that mental ill-health is the most enduring health taboo, but yet one of the most commonly experienced health problems.

'Discrimination is the single biggest problem for mental health policy. How many people recover and establish themselves in the community if they are constantly refused a chance to work or contribute to society?

'Despite the fact that one in four people in the UK will have a mental health problem this year, this report uncovers how ingrained, entrenched and debilitating attitudes towards mental ill-health still are.'

Judi Clements,
Mind's National Director

Daily life – in public

Almost half (47%) of respondents had been harassed or abused in public because of their mental health problems. Many people had been shouted at in the street and threatened, whilst some had actually been physically attacked.

Some very disturbing threats were made to people, including knife attacks and beatings, but more common were experiences of degrading harassment and bullying in public.

Several people said they had windows broken, or eggs or stones thrown at them. Both local children and adults ridiculed people in public, but more respondents mentioned young people and children as the culprits.

Men were more likely to experience harassment or abuse in public than woman – 53% of men compared to 40% of women.

'I work very hard at pulling myself out of a depression and then get threatened and abused by a gang of kids

---

Q. Have you ever experienced harassment or abuse in public because of your mental health problems?

Yes	47%
Shouted at in the street	29%
Threatened	21%
Physically attacked	14%
Forced to leave premises	16%

By Mind Region/Wales:

Northern	42%	South East	46%
North West	55%	South West	53%
Trent & Yorks	44%	Wales	40%
West Mids	50%		

Q. Have you ever actually been harassed or attacked?

Yes	49%
By neighbours and other tenants	21%
By strangers	20%
By landlords (private & public)	7%

By Mind Region/Wales:

Northern	37%	South East	56%
North West	49%	South West	44%
Trent & Yorks	49%	Wales	37%
West Mids	50%		

Q. Have you ever felt threatened, or afraid of attack?

Yes	57%
Inside my own home	25%
Outside in my immediate neighbourhood	34%

By Mind Region/Wales:

Northern	51%	South East	56%
North West	65%	South West	58%
Trent & Yorks	61%	Wales	53%
West Mids	55%		

Q. Have you ever been forced to move home because of harassment linked to your mental health problems?

Yes	26%

By Mind Region/Wales:

Northern	19%	South East	24%
North West	34%	South West	32%
Trent & Yorks	25%	Wales	25%
West Mids	25%		

on the way home from my first walk out in weeks. My son is with me. He is also attacked. I lose credibility in his eyes, and in my own eyes. Mud and stones are thrown at us. Hurt and angry, I think "What's the point in trying to get better?"'

Woman aged 43, diagnosed with depression, South East

'Children have thrown stones at my windows and fruit at me in the street.'

Man aged 41, diagnosed with schizophrenia, Trent & Yorkshire

'Various gangs in the district call me "nutter" and spit at me. The gangs on the estate got to know I was a psychiatric outpatient so I am teased and harassed.'

(Man aged 71, no diagnosis given, North West)

'Strangers come up to me and want to fight me. Being black with mental health problems has affected me.'

(Woman aged 31, no diagnosis given, South East)

Daily life – at home

Over half (57%) of the people felt afraid of attack, with almost as many people actually being harassed or attacked.

At its worst people were living in fear inside their own homes. Some people told of how their flats had been burgled or broken into and one person had lit matches put through their letter-box. Others had dog's muck, used condoms and abusive letters stuffed through their front doors.

Many people said how afraid they felt outside in their local communities. Almost half the people had actually been harassed or attacked at home or in their neighbourhoods, many by neighbours and strangers as well as local children and young people.

Some people had been attacked by their partners and others by their landlords. People in authority including the police and social workers were also mentioned. Some people commented on the harassment they had suffered from other patients and staff when their home was a hospital.

'I love the small town where I lived, and where my son was born, but I was afraid he would get name called as I often was, so we moved to a larger town where we could be more relaxed and not known. I have suffered more because of ignorance of certain people than I have throughout my actual mental health problems.'

(Mother aged 26, diagnosed with clinical depression and psychosis, Trent & Yorkshire)

'My house was broken into five times in six months. I was shouted at and threatened and scared to stay in my house, or go out. I was really scared. I've moved and I hope things will be OK now. It's not fair on us – the people who do this should think. They may need psychiatric help themselves one day.'

(Woman aged 38, diagnosed with depression, Northern England)

'A friend had a poster saying "danger paranoid schizophrenic within" pinned to her flat's door.'

(Man aged 37, diagnosed with schizophrenia, depression, South East)

'I've had paint on my front door, windows broken, verbal abuse, stones thrown at me by kids on the street, dirty clothes put on my doorstep and I've had lit newspaper put through my letter-box.'

(Woman aged 50, diagnosed with manic depression, West Midlands)

Summary of key findings

- A third of people (34%) said they had been dismissed or forced to resign from jobs
- 69% of people had been put off applying for jobs for fear of unfair treatment
- Almost half (47%) the people had been abused or harassed in public, and 14% had been physically attacked
- A quarter (25%) of people felt at risk of attack inside their own homes
- 26% of people were forced to move home because of harassment
- Almost a quarter (24%) of parents said their children had been teased or bullied, or that they were afraid it would happen
- 25% of people had been turned down by insurance or finance companies
- Half (50%) of people felt unfairly treated by general health care services
- A third (33%) complained that their GP had treated them unfairly
- 45% of people thought that discrimination had increased in the last five years compared with 18% who thought it had decreased

• The above is an extract from *Not Just Sticks & Stones* by Jim Read and Sue Baker, November 1996, published by Mind. See page 39 for address details. ©*Mind, 1997*

The baby blues and postnatal depression

One in two women who have just given birth experiences the baby blues. This article explains why some women feel emotional after a birth and it offers information and advice about the blues and postnatal depression

The baby blues

After the birth of a baby about half of all mothers suffer a period of mild depression called the blues. This may last for a few hours or, at most, for a few days and then it disappears.

Symptoms of the blues

Many mothers feel very emotional and upset when they have the blues and they cry for no particular reason. They may find that it is impossible to cheer up. Some mothers feel very anxious and tense. Minor problems may cause mothers with the blues to worry a great deal.

Some mothers have pains for which there is no medical cause or they may feel unwell but without any particular symptoms. Most mothers who have the blues feel very tired and lethargic most of the time. Frequently mothers who have the blues have difficulty sleeping.

Possible causes of the blues

The blues may have several causes, some biological and some emotional.

When a baby is born there are very sudden changes in the mother's hormone levels. Some, required during pregnancy, drop rapidly, while others, like those which start the production of milk, rise. These rapid changes may act to trigger the blues.

Many mothers are unprepared for the extreme weariness which often follows a birth. The weariness is usually due to a combination of factors. In many cases the mother will have been anticipating the birth with some apprehension. This, as well as the physical exertion of the birth itself, can make mothers feel exhausted.

Rest and quiet are most important after a birth. Few mothers get either, as they are busy responding to the needs of the baby, or, when they might be able to rest, they are disturbed by hospital or home routines or by visitors who may stay too long.

Sometimes the baby may have a slight health problem such as jaundice or feeding difficulties in the early days. These problems are very common with new babies, but they cause mothers great anxiety. The problems do settle down as the baby gets older and mothers should try to talk to medical staff and allow themselves to be reassured that the baby will thrive.

What can be done to help a blues sufferer?

Mothers who have the blues should be allowed to cry if they want to and allowed to express their fluctuating emotions. If they feel miserable they should not be told to pull themselves together. It can be a great help to the mother if someone listens to her and reassures her that her worries and misery will not last and that she will soon feel better.

A mother who has the blues must have as much rest as possible. It may also help the mother if she is told that the blues are very common and that they will usually pass quickly.

Affected mothers are often over-sensitive about what is said to them by relatives and medical staff. So tact and empathy from the staff can be very beneficial at this time.

Length of the blues

In most cases the blues last for only a few days and then the feelings fade.

If the blues do continue and seem to be getting worse then the mother should see her doctor and discuss the problem.

Postnatal depression

Postnatal depression is an unpleasant illness which affects about 10% of mothers who have recently given birth. The depression often starts after the mother has left hospital and been discharged by the midwife.

Symptoms of postnatal depression

Postnatal depression has many symptoms. Most mothers who have the illness find that they are less able to cope with the demands of the baby and of the home. Some mothers feel very despondent. They may feel very anxious and fearful, they worry about their own health and that of the baby. They may suffer from panic attacks and feel tense and irritable all the time. Most depressed mothers feel tired and lack energy, often they feel unable to concentrate and they find even simple tasks are confusing and demand too much energy.

Some mothers experience pains for which there is no cause (other than tension and anxiety), many suffer difficulty in sleeping and poor appetite. Many depressed mothers lose interest in sex.

A depressed mother may suffer from any or all of the symptoms mentioned. Most mothers who have this illness feel guilty that they are not 'coping' as they feel they should be.

What can be done if you have postnatal depression?

If your depression lasts longer than a few days you should discuss your feelings with your doctor. If possible take your partner or a friend or relative with you. Before you see the doctor write a list of all the symptoms that you are suffering from. You should not go on suffering depression in the hope that it will go away. Postnatal depression is a real illness and it can be treated successfully with anti-depressant drugs. These drugs are not addictive. They make the unpleasant symptoms fade until they go completely.

Who else can help?

After you have seen the doctor, you may find it helpful to talk to an understanding and sympathetic member of your family or a friend. If your friend understands that you will recover completely and be your 'old self' again when you are better, then he or she can be a real source of comfort and reassurance to you during the time of your illness.

Your midwife, district nurse and health visitor can also give you advice, reassurance and support.

It is important to remember that all mothers recover from postnatal depression. As the recovery proceeds, the bad days get fewer and less upsetting and the good days become more numerous. Gradually the bad days disappear completely.

Some mothers find it helpful to talk to a mother who has had postnatal depression and recovered. If you write to the Association for Postnatal Illness, we will send you further information about the illness and tell you how to apply for a supporter who has had the illness.

Self-help

Although it may be very difficult to rest when you have a demanding baby and perhaps other children to care for, it does help to rest as much as possible if you are suffering from depression. You will find that you feel worse if you are overtired. Ask a partner or friend to care for the baby whilst you have a proper rest, preferably in the middle of the day. Try to lie on your bed even if you do not sleep. A rest in the day often improves sleeping at night for those with sleeping difficulties.

Try to eat a small meal or have a hot sweet drink at regular intervals. Many depressed mothers forget to eat and this can make the depression symptoms feel worse.

Further information

For more information about postnatal depression please write to:

The Association for Postnatal Illness, 25 Jerdan Place, Fulham, London SW6 1BE. Telephone 0171-386 0868. 10am – 5pm, Monday – Friday. Please enclose a stamped addressed envelope.

If you would like to join a group meeting where all the problems of motherhood are discussed please write to:

The National Childbirth Trust, Alexandra House, Oldham Terrace, Acton, London W3 6NH. Telephone 0181-992 8637

Meet-a-Mum Association, 14 Willis Road, Croydon, Surrey CR0 2XX. Telephone 0181-665 0357

© Association for Post-natal Illness
March, 1997

Mental health and older people

What are mental health problems?

Problems such as feelings of depression, anxiety and confusion affect most people at some time, particularly after a distressing life event. Mental health problems arise when these symptoms occur to such an extent or for such a long period of time that they make it difficult to cope with everyday life.

Older people may be particularly vulnerable to such feelings, especially if they have suffered a bereavement, have problems with mobility or are feeling lonely or isolated. Older people are also far more at risk of developing some form of dementia.

How many older people are affected by mental health problems?

2 in 10 (10.6m) of the UK population are over retirement age – by the year 2000, 1.2 million people will be over 85. An ageing population brings with it increasing rates of mental ill-health, particularly in the over-85 age group.

5% of all people over retirement age and 25% of people over 85 currently suffer from clinical dementia. 1.5 million people over 65 are affected by depression.

Studies show that only a quarter of dementia sufferers are known to GPs and 1 in 10 to psychiatrists. Virtually no depressed older people are known to GPs or to the psychiatric services.

How are older people affected by depression?

For some older people depression can be brought on by physical ill-health. The constant pain of arthritis and other conditions associated with ageing can leave people feeling desperately unhappy and isolated. GPs should always be consulted about medication and physiotherapy which can relieve many of the symptoms of these conditions and lead to greater independence and a better quality of life.

For other older people depression can be triggered by life changes such as bereavement or having to move into sheltered or residential accommodation or by loneliness or money worries.

Symptoms of depression include feelings of sadness which seem impossible to overcome and a loss of interest in life and activities. Motivation and drive can be lost as people feel that they do not have the energy to achieve even limited tasks. People can become withdrawn, have difficulty sleeping and even contemplate suicide. Anyone experiencing these feelings should talk to their GP as treatments and specialist sources of help are available.

What are the symptoms of dementia?

Symptoms vary between individuals, but initial problems usually relate to the loss of short-term memory. Sufferers may be able to remember events from the past, but have difficulty in remembering what they did only a few hours ago. They may also fail to recognise places or forget names of friends or family.

People with dementia often lose interest in their usual hobbies or pastimes and may appear apathetic or unmotivated. They can have difficulty grasping new ideas and so become frightened of change and unwilling to try new things.

Some people may also become moody or aggressive as they realise that they are no longer able to do things which in the past they have taken for granted.

Who cares for older people with mental health problems?

Day centres and residential homes provide care for some people suffering from dementia or severe depression. However, as only 25% of dementia sufferers are known to GPs, the majority of people are cared for at home by family members. Research

---

Research has shown that 1.6 million adults spend up to 20 hours a week caring for dependants with mental health problems

---

has shown that 1.6 million adults spend up to 20 hours a week caring for dependants with mental health problems in their own homes or other households.

Where can carers get support?

Carers should be in contact with their GP who can provide advice about medication and put them in touch with specialist services where necessary. GPs also have a responsibility to offer all patients an annual health check covering physical health and an assessment of mental functions such as memory and mood. If necessary, a GP can allocate a health visitor or district nurse to make home visits.

Social Services Departments can also be contacted either directly

---

or through a GP. They will carry out an assessment of needs and may assign a home help or offer a place at a day centre. Unlike GP services, social services such as these are not always provided free. Carers can find out what is available and what costs are involved through their GP or local authority.

Voluntary organisations are also able to offer advice and support and many have carers' support groups.

• The Mental Health Foundation supports research and innovative community projects working with older people with mental health problems. The Foundation has recently published a booklet – *Because You Care* – to help carers cope with difficult behaviour in people with dementia. Copies of this booklet and further information about the work of the Foundation are available from the Information Office, The Mental Health Foundation, 37 Mortimer Street, London W1N 8JU. Tel 0171 580 0145.

(Figures taken from *Mental Illness: the fundamental facts*. Published in 1993 and available from the Mental Health Foundation at £4.50.)

© *Mental Health Foundation*

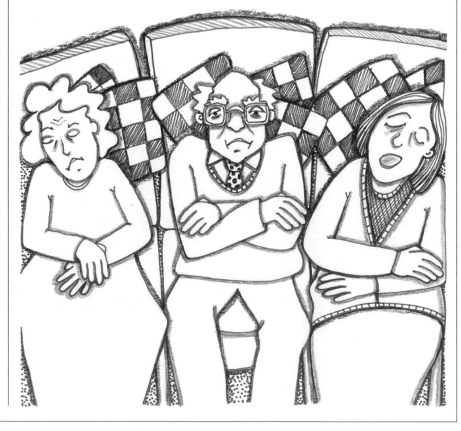

Drug that can ease the misery of Alzheimer's

By Jenny Hope, Medical Correspondent

The first NHS drug treatment for Alzheimer's disease could be available soon.

The new medicine can alleviate early symptoms of memory loss and disrupted thought processes, without serious side-effects.

Aricept was approved by US licensing authorities last month after trials involving more than 1,000 patients. Researchers found it improved memory and the ability to think in one out of two patients with mild to moderate Alzheimer's.

Side-effects, which included nausea, diarrhoea, fatigue and muscle cramps, were usually not serious and short-term.

Aricept is still being considered for a British licence, with a decision expected within four months. There is no NHS treatment available for the disease, symptoms of which include fluctuations in memory, repetition of questions and eccentric behaviour.

Tacrine, the only other Alzheimer's drug available in the US, was refused a British licence in March 1995.

Although no reasons were given for its rejection, it appeared that the benefits were outweighed by the risk of side-effects, including liver damage.

Alzheimer's disease still carries a stigma despite affecting many public figures. Former US president Ronald Reagan highlighted the issues when he announced he had the disease. Former England football manager Sir Alf Ramsey is another sufferer.

Neither Tacrine nor Aricept cures Alzheimer's. They stop the breakdown of a brain chemical which allows nerve impulses to be passed along and is highly important in memory. Sufferers have depleted supplies of the brain chemicals and, in the short term, the drugs can improve communication between brain cells.

Of the 500,000 Britons with Alzheimer's, it is thought 180,000 patients with the mild to moderate form of the disease would benefit from Aricept. At lest 300 Britons at 30 hospitals are taking it as part of an international clinical trial.

Professor Alistair Burns, of the School of Psychiatry at Manchester University, said: 'There are undoubtedly people it helps.

'Alzheimer's is a disease for which there is currently no treatment so it is important for patients and their families to know this has encouraging potential in the mild to moderate stages of the disease.

'It is not a miracle cure but sometimes treatments that offer modest advances are the ones that stand the test of time.'

© The Daily Mail
January, 1997

Dementia in perspective

- 650,000 people in the UK have Alzheimer's or another type of dementia.

- Each year an estimated 180,000 people in this country develop dementia; one in twenty of those aged 65 or more, and one in five of the over-80s.

- Dementia is being detected in growing numbers of younger people. In the UK 17,000 of those with the condition are under 65.

- 154,000 people with dementia live alone. By the year 2011 this figure is expected to rise to 245,000.

- The Alzheimer's Disease Society provides support for those suffering from any form of dementia and those who care for them.

© Alzheimer's Disease Society

Percentage of elderly population who develop dementia

Aged 65 or more

Aged over 80

0   5   10   15   20%

Source: Alzheimer's Disease Society

Alzheimer's disease – what is it?

Alzheimer's disease is a physical disease which causes a progressive decline in the abilities to remember, learn, understand, communicate and reason. It is the most common type of dementia and was first described by Alois Alzheimer, a German neurologist, in 1907. There are a number of different forms of Alzheimer's disease.

Dementia

Dementia is a condition characterised by a progressive loss of mental abilities accompanied by changes in behaviour and a gradual loss of the skills needed to carry out ordinary daily activities. There are a number of different types of dementia.

It is estimated that there are 650,000 people with dementia in the UK and that 50 to 60 per cent of this number have conditions that fit into the category of Alzheimer's disease. Others have dementia in which vascular disease appears to be prominent in the development, while a small number have a dementia that is secondary to another condition. Also, studies of Diffuse Lewy body disease suggest that it may account for 10 to 15 per cent of cases of dementia.

The likelihood of developing dementia increases as people get older. It affects less than one person in a thousand of those below the age of 65 and between four and five in a hundred of all those over 65. However, within the over-65 age group there is a strong increase in the rate with age, with about 2 per cent of those between 65 and 75 suffering from dementia, rising to over 20 per cent of those over 80.

Alzheimer's disease

Symptoms

The symptoms of Alzheimer's disease vary from individual to individual.

In the early stages you may notice that the person is more forgetful of recent events, or more likely to repeat themselves in conversation, less concerned with activities or other people, less able to grasp new ideas or adapt to change, more anxious about having to make decisions, or more irritable or upset if they cannot manage a task. It may be hard to distinguish these signs from reactions which can occur after a bereavement, for example, or when someone is under stress.

As the disease progresses problems will become more apparent. The loss of short-term memory is likely to become more obvious and people with Alzheimer's often become confused about time or place, thinking night is day or becoming lost. They may find it harder to carry out simple tasks and it may become more difficult to understand what they are saying or for them to understand you. They may become angry, agitated, upset or withdrawn, or behave oddly. In later stages they may no longer be able to recognise those who are close to them and become increasingly dependent on others for care.

The course of the disease varies from one person to another. The decline can be rapid in some people and more gradual in others.

Diagnosis

If you are worried because your relative seems confused or unlike themselves, visit your GP straight away. There are a number of conditions, apart from dementia, which may be causing this behaviour, many of which can be treated. Only after excluding other possible conditions, usually through a series of tests, will a diagnosis of dementia be made. The GP may refer your relative to a specialist or you can ask to be referred.

To help in reaching a diagnosis the doctor is likely to spend time talking to a relative or close friend about any changes they have observed. They will also need to talk to the patient and observe their behaviour. This is often best carried out in the home setting.

As yet there is no medical test for Alzheimer's disease. The diagnosis can only be confirmed with certainty through examining the brain at a post mortem.

Treatment

Although a great deal of research is being carried out there is at present no curative treatment for Alzheimer's disease. However, it is important to get a probable diagnosis as soon as possible as this will give the patient and carer access to support services that can improve their quality of life and lessen the strain (see information sheet no. 15, *Services: who can help?*). Professionals and other carers may also be able to suggest many helpful coping strategies or you may find the Alzheimer's Disease Society advice sheets helpful. However, remember that services and strategies which are suitable for older people with dementia may differ from those appropriate for younger people.

Research

Research has shown that Alzheimer's disease is associated with the abnormal function of brain cells. Changes within the brain, referred to as tangles and plaques, can occur with normal ageing but are more widespread and greater in number among people with Alzheimer's. The tangles consist of fibrillary protein abnormalities and the plaques are associated with deposits of another abnormal protein, ß-amyloid.

Causes

The causes of Alzheimer's disease are not yet fully understood although a great deal of research is going on. It seems likely that in many cases there are a number of different contributory factors. These may differ in different people. Although it seems clear that the majority of cases occurs sporadically, that is where no known family history of Alzheimer's exists, a genetic cause has been found in a very small number of families, approximately 5 per cent. Scientists have identified a number of genes linked to these cases. The majority of cases is linked to chromosome 14 and has a particularly aggressive form of the disease with onset in the 40s. The finding of these genetic links is important because it will soon be possible to do predictive testing for this form of dementia. It is also now known that there is an inherited risk factor for late-onset Alzheimer's disease. Everyone carries a version of a protein called apolipoprotein E. Inheritance of the ApoE4 allele is associated with an earlier onset age of Alzheimer's disease whilst inheritance of the ApoE2 allele decreases the risk of developing the disease. This finding cannot be used for predictive testing of individuals.

There also seems to be some evidence that serious head injury may play a part in the development of Alzheimer's in a small number of cases. Other research into causes includes looking at the possible effect of environmental variables such as nutrition and the absorption of metals, at viruses and the role of the body's immune system.

Diagnosis

Although no simple test for Alzheimer's has been devised, research being carried out includes looking for changes in the brain through different types of scan and looking for abnormal changes in the cerebral spinal fluid.

Treatment

Research currently being carried out into possible treatments for Alzheimer's disease includes looking at neuro-transmitters and examining abnormal protein synthesis and its effect on brain cells.

Carers

Dementia also has a profound effect on the lives of family members and close friends. It is important to remember that dementia is nothing to be ashamed of and that it is nobody's fault, particularly if you come from a background where such illness is not usually discussed outside the family. If you are the main carer it is important to get support for yourself and to remember you are an individual with needs of your own.

The Alzheimer's Disease Society can offer advice and information and put you in touch with your nearest branch or support group to help you find out more about local services and support.

• The above is an extract from *Alzheimer's Disease – what is it?*, produced by the Alzheimer's Disease Society. See page 39 for address details. © *Alzheimer's Disease Society May, 1996*

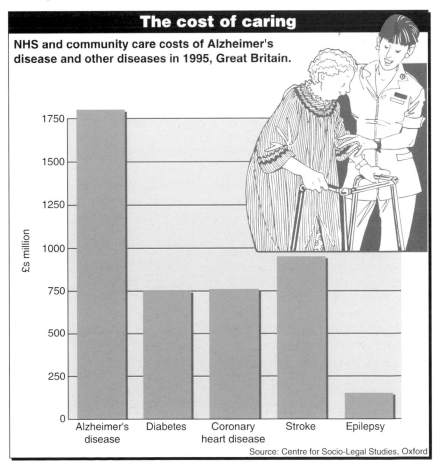

The cost of caring

NHS and community care costs of Alzheimer's disease and other diseases in 1995, Great Britain.

£s million

Alzheimer's disease | Diabetes | Coronary heart disease | Stroke | Epilepsy

Source: Centre for Socio-Legal Studies, Oxford

Can you tell me something about schizophrenia?

Information from the Schizophrenia Association of Great Britain (SAGB)

What is schizophrenia?

Nobody knows what schizophrenia is except that it is an illness which affects the chemistry of the brain. It affects thinking, emotions and behaviour. Changes in personality develop as a result of the illness.

In the Schizophrenia Association of Great Britain we think schizophrenia is an umbrella term covering a number of physical diseases of the body and brain which eventually disturb the proper functioning of the brain and give rise to the main psychiatric symptoms. In some cases, perhaps in all, there is a genetic vulnerability to develop such illnesses. We have adopted an umbrella as our logo, thus pictorially defining our belief that schizophrenia is not one disease but many which share in common only the psychiatric symptoms.

How is schizophrenia recognised?

A very slow change in personality is the chief indication of the development of a schizophrenic illness. Only those very close to the patient can recognise something serious is happening to him/her. Most of the time, especially outside the family, he/she may seem totally normal. When the family eventually goes to the doctor for help they are at their wits' end with worry. The doctor may say, if the patient is an adolescent, that what they report is just part of growing up. This is small comfort to the family. The patient also may not recognise he has changed and may think it is the family who has become peculiar.

There is no biochemical test for schizophrenia. The doctor is not prepared to diagnose it until the severe symptoms of hallucinations, delusions and thought disorder develop and the patient and family

may be left to suffer for years without medical help. With all other diseases it is thought to be of huge importance to diagnose as early as possible so that treatment can start and deterioration be prevented. The opposite occurs in schizophrenia. Deterioration of the illness is waited for and, when it occurs, it is less easy to treat.

Early signs and symptoms of schizophrenia

It is not easy to know that the early changes observed by relatives are indicators of the onset of a major, severe, psychiatric disease like schizophrenia. It is however important to know the sort of things that may occur and which have been reported. We learned a lot about the early symptoms from the members of the SAGB and from early textbooks when their importance was recognised and understood. Some of these early symptoms are physical and some

are behavioural. There is a mixture of reported symptoms. Not all will be observed in any one patient. The importance of these early symptoms is immense. They can tell us of the physical nature of schizophrenia before the advanced symptoms affect the brain and its proper functioning. The severity of the advanced brain symptoms makes doctors concentrate on them above all else and the early physical symptoms are forgotten. We believe they are of prime importance. A decrease in concentration may occur, particularly noticeable if the patient is in school or college, and as a result, starts to fail his examinations. He may become exhausted during the day and overactive at night, cooking for himself and playing very loud music. He may eat alone and not with the family. He may isolate himself and neglect himself. He may take drugs and alcohol to relieve the oncoming schizophrenic symptoms. These will make his condition much worse. He may become irritable, irrational, angry and violent. He may change his beliefs and become very

religious where once he was a non-believer. He may become a socialist where once he was a conservative or vice versa. He may become very suspicious of his family and friends. At first symptoms may only show when he is tired. Most of the time he will be normal. He may begin to smoke heavily. He may lose weight dramatically and look very pale, gaunt and ill. He may have many digestive problems with nausea, vomiting, diarrhoea or constipation. Blood pressure may be high or low, breathing may be shallow, and posture poor. There may be frequent incapacitating flu-like infections with a slightly raised temperature. The patient may have cravings for sweet things and junk foods. Eventually the major psychiatric symptoms may be brought on by a severe viral infection like measles, influenza or glandular fever.

Late symptoms

No one could fail to recognise the seriousness of the late symptoms and a psychiatrist will diagnose schizophrenia when hallucinations, delusions and thought disorder are present.

1. Hallucinations. These may be:
a) auditory – patients hear voices commenting, instructing and sometimes telling them to do awful things. These are the patient's own pathological thoughts which may be persistent and tormenting. Patients can learn to tell their voices to go away and, even if they do not do so, the fact of their telling them reduces their importance. They should never act on what the voices say. If patients talk aloud their voices often go.

b) visual – patients see people who are not there or they might see the world as distorted – the walls, for example, might seem to breathe.

c) smell and taste – may be altered and the patient may smell something cooking when nothing is cooking, or he may think he is being poisoned because his food tastes different.

2. Delusions
These are false beliefs which no amount of reasoning will dislodge. They may be the cause of many tragedies. For example, someone may believe their husband or wife is being unfaithful when there is no basis for this. The patients' delusions may be paranoid and their suspicions may be widespread or directed at one or two people, mainly those closest to them. They may believe they are being persecuted and that people are out to get them. They may become totally panic-stricken and afraid. The patient may harm someone he loves because of this huge fear and panic. Sometimes the delusions are grandiose and the patient may imagine he is, for example, Christ or the King.

3. Thought disorder
The patient's thoughts may be jumbled. Patients may not be able to complete a sentence. Their concentration may be very poor. Sometimes they may have a blank mind, with no thoughts.

However overwhelming these final symptoms are, they are not the cause of schizophrenia. They let us know that the functions of the brain have been altered by disease whether originating in the brain (as for example with a brain tumour or meningitis) or more likely in the body.

What causes schizophrenia?

No one knows as yet. A number of research programmes are being developed to try to find out. We are carrying out research into genetic and biochemical causes for schizophrenia. Whatever the cause it is no one's fault. It is nothing to do with the way the patient was brought up. The causes are physical.

Does it run in the family?

It does usually run in families and can often be traced from generation to generation. On the other hand the illness can crop up in a family apparently out of the blue. It is commonly accepted that there is a genetic vulnerability to schizophrenia. If you need to know more about possible genetic risk advice is available from us.

When does it usually start?

Schizophrenia can occur at any age, even in childhood, but it generally shows itself in adolescence or early adulthood. It usually starts earlier in males and is a more severe illness in males.

Will they get better?

Drugs are available which lessen the psychiatric symptoms. There is as yet no 'magic' cure. Some people remain well if they continue to take medication as prescribed by the doctor. Others have a less predictable course. If the patient were regularly given a thorough physical investigation it might be found he had a medical condition. If this were then successfully treated both the physical and mental symptoms might get better.

I have never met anyone with schizophrenia

One in every hundred people has schizophrenia. It is probable that you do know people with the illness without realising it.

How is it treated?

With drugs called neuroleptics. There is a wide range of these drugs. In many cases neuroleptics can control symptoms effectively. Neuroleptics cannot cure schizophrenia but they can make the patient a lot better and more able to cope with life. They are strong drugs and unfortunately many people will suffer side-effects. It is necessary with the drug clozapine (Clorazil) to have regular blood tests as this drug can be very toxic to some people. Lithium carbonate also has to be monitored in the blood. SAGB newsletters frequently contain up-to-date information on drug treatments.

Bodily diseases

As we believe a number of bodily diseases can cause the psychiatric symptoms in schizophrenia it is essential that patients have regular and thorough physical examinations as noted above.

Gastro-intestinal disease, cardiovascular disease, endocrine disease and infections may be particularly commonly found in schizophrenia and be the cause of the schizophrenic symptoms or may worsen them. We in SAGB have bought an automatic analyser which will measure 14 different biochemical parameters from a finger-prick of blood. The results may indicate the presence of bodily disease.

Nutritional factors

It is highly likely that nutrition is of great importance in schizophrenia. If the gut and other membranes are damaged because of one or more genetic defects then it may be particularly important to eat the right foods to put the least stress on the defect. Particular fats may be important and in view of the high incidence of coeliac disease in families where there is schizophrenia, avoiding wheat and milk may be helpful. Gut damage was found in schizophrenics in the 1940s and 1950s similar to that found in coeliac disease. Such gut damage causes a malabsorption of nutrients and thus vitamins, especially B12 and folic acid, may be needed but other vitamins and minerals also are needed if malabsorption is found.

It is highly likely that nutrition is of great importance in schizophrenia

As heart disease is said to be twice as common in schizophrenics as in the general population and as a magnesium salt is increasingly being given for heart disease and used to be used for mania, it would perhaps be wise for patients with panic, violence and anger particularly to take a magnesium supplement obtainable from a chemist or health food shop. Finally, the medications used to treat schizophrenia lower levels of many vitamins in the blood. They

also lower magnesium (another reason to take one of its compounds). Perhaps all patients should take magnesium unless they have kidney disease, when it is contraindicated.

What do I do if I feel worried about something or I need explanation, advice or help?

Ring us: (01248 354048) or write: Schizophrenia Association of Great Britain, Bryn Hyfryd, The Crescent, Bangor, Gwynedd. LL57 2AG.

Someone will be in the office from 9am – 4pm most weekdays (01248 354048)

If you would like to join a group of carers and patients then there is another organisation which can help you with this. Contact: National Schizophrenia Fellowship, 28 Castle Street, Kingston upon Thames. KT1S 1SS. Telephone 0181 974 6814 (10am – 3pm)

© The Schizophrenia Association of Great Britain (SAGB)

Living with schizophrenia

'Red-hot voices howling in my mind.' That's how Sarah Jones, 32, describes her mental illness. Here she and her husband David, 35, talk about the challenges and torments of schizophrenia

By Jo Mears

Sarah: I had my first schizophrenic attack when I was 27. David and I were married and were both working as research assistants. I'd never been seriously mentally ill before, although I'd suffered from depression since the age of eight. My family found it hard to talk about feelings and I never communicated well with my parents.

The attack happened after a bout of depression. I'd been finding it hard to concentrate at work and would curl up in the staff toilet during the day. I wasn't eating properly, was waking early in the morning and would hardly talk to anyone – the usual symptoms of depression.

Then I started hearing voices that seemed to come from outside my head. They began tormenting

me, telling me I was evil, that I'd be better off dead. They were male and female voices who'd talk about me and to me, sometimes jeering and laughing. It sounds bizarre, but it doesn't occur to you that it's your mind playing tricks. In the end I couldn't stand it – I took an overdose of antidepressants to blot them out.

After that I spent a week in our local psychiatric hospital as a voluntary patient. David was supportive, making sure I got my own cubicle and bringing me cream cakes and books. When I came home I think he thought that would be the

end of it, but within four months I was back in hospital. Schizophrenia was eventually diagnosed. It was a relief to know what it was.

There are lots of symptoms of schizophrenia, such as being withdrawn, unmotivated and not caring about your appearance. But the most well-known ones are hearing voices and having delusions. Hearing voices is when you experience your thoughts as if they're coming from outside your head. Delusions are when you have a fixed belief in something, even though common sense tells you it can't be true. Your logic goes. Some people have hallucinations that are forms of distorted vision – metal paperclips look like insects to me, or I think I see people about three-feet high with round, moon-like faces.

At times I've been so scared that I've rushed out of the house and wandered the streets trying to escape. Once I was sure I was going to be conscripted into the Filipino army, so I went to a supermarket where I thought I'd be anonymous. Another time I was convinced Gadaffi had dropped a bomb on Newcastle and was terrified to leave my home. You can't explain it. Your brain and reason lose track of each other.

The worst aspect of schizophrenia is the danger it can put you in. Once I was attacked by a man when I was wandering the streets at three in the morning. I think he wanted to rape me. I fought him off and he slashed my arms and face with a knife. When David saw me bandaged up in the hospital he stayed calm. He didn't ask me what had happened, just waited until I was able to tell him.

Most of the time when I'm ill I'm aware of what's going on around me and can remember it afterwards. But a few year ago I went through a stage of blacking out and finding myself in horrifying situations.

Once I woke up to find myself wading out to sea, another time I only came to when I hit the water after jumping off a bridge into the Tyne. Luckily I was swept to the edge by the current. When I come to, it's often like coming out of a nightmare – only the nightmare's been real. Whenever David's been really worried about me he's locked me in the house or taken me back to the hospital. He's been a lifeline.

The police are more aware of mental illness these days, so if they find me wandering around they take me straight to the local hospital. But in the past I've been treated badly and thrown in a cell. Once they handcuffed me even though my wrists were bleeding from where I'd cut them. I felt terribly humiliated.

I once lashed out at a policeman because he frightened me, but that's the only time I've ever tried to hurt someone else. Most of the time my anger and confusion are directed inwards. I'd cut my wrists or carve the word Evil into my arms because the voices were telling me to. Because of the state I was in it didn't hurt, and in a way it seemed to relieve

some of the unbearable pressure.

People often believe, mistakenly, that everyone who suffers from schizophrenia is violent. Although some are, the majority would never be violent to anyone other than themselves. I've tried to commit suicide several times – sometimes because I don't know what I'm doing and other times because I'm fed up with feeling like this. Ten per cent of schizophrenics commit suicide and I've already lost five friends who suffered from the same illness.

At times I've been so scared that I've rushed out of the house and wandered the streets trying to escape

---

It's ten years since my first admission to hospital and since then I've been back 20 times. We've discovered my illness goes through phases, which helps. I don't always know what sparks it off, but I know that in the winter and at Christmas I can be particularly vulnerable.

Over the past couple of years I've improved considerably. I'm better at recognising when an attack

is coming on and take myself to hospital before I do anything stupid. Stress can also be a trigger, so I go to aerobics, practise meditation and use aromatherapy to relieve it. I see a psychiatrist who prescribes me Sulpiride – a sedative used to control acute hallucinations and delusions – which makes me feel as though I'm experiencing everything through cotton wool. Other antipsychotic drugs have had much worse effects on me, like muscle spasms and terrible restlessness.

Louise, my social worker, has been a great help. She's drawn up a contract whereby I agree not to hurt myself and in return she counsels me. I'm proud that I've stuck to it and it's helping to restore my self-esteem.

David's brilliant. He helps me keep to a regular timetable of eating and sleeping and is incredibly patient and supportive. Going through this together has definitely deepened our relationship.

I'm lucky that I'm able to lead a fairly normal life. Many people with schizophrenia become isolated and this makes them withdraw into themselves even more. David and I do most things ordinary couples do. I'm aware I've put him under incredible strain and I'd have understood if he'd left me – although I'd have been heartbroken. I know

people whose schizophrenia has burned itself out by their forties and at the moment I'm clinging to the hope that I might be one of those.

David: I fell in love with Sarah because she had lots of energy and great emotional and spiritual depth. We had a lot in common – we worked in the same field of research and had a similar philosophy on life. We went out together for six months before we got engaged, and then married a year later.

The first I knew about Sarah's illness was when I got a call from one of her colleagues to say she'd gone into hospital after taking an overdose of antidepressants. I was angry that no one had mentioned anything sooner. That probably sounds odd, but Sarah had always suffered from depression on and off, so I was used to her being moody. What I didn't know was that for several weeks she'd been acting strangely at work – being withdrawn and talking to herself. Looking back I should have noticed. But I was wrapped up in my work – besides, Sarah was behaving normally at home.

At the hospital I was very confused. I wasn't sure what to do, so I decided the best thing was to be as supportive as possible. I thought it would blow over, but it wasn't until six months later that schizophrenia was diagnosed. I knew that, chemically, people with schizophrenia are thought to have excess dopamine receptors in their brain (a protein allowing messages to travel around the brain) and that this is reduced by taking antipsychotic drugs. No one knows exactly what causes it, although there is a genetic link, and environmental factors seem to play a role. But no one in either of our families had suffered from mental illness, so I didn't know what to expect. In the beginning I clung to the hope that it was just a passing phase and that Sarah would soon recover.

I was wrong. After Sarah's first stay in hospital she was better for four months, then she was re-admitted. It was the start of a cycle of behaviour common in schizophrenics, where they're better for a while, then suffer a relapse and end

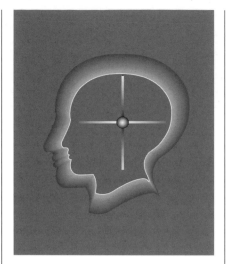

up in hospital again. Sarah's illness seemed to bring new and increasingly bizarre behaviour with every turn. Obviously the suicide attempts were distressing, but what worried me most was the way she'd wander the streets for hours in a confused state. Sometimes she'd disappear for days and I'd lie in bed waiting to hear her key in the lock. It was no good calling the police because they wouldn't know where to find her. I was always so relieved to know she was safe.

No one in either of our families had suffered from mental illness, so I didn't know what to expect

---

At first I couldn't bear sitting around waiting so I visited the places I knew she went. I walked for hours looking for her. The worst time was when I came home to find a blood-stained dress in the bin. She'd been wandering the streets and a man had slashed her with a knife. It gave me a terrible fright.

But I couldn't watch her 24 hours a day. If I knew she was ill I was happy for her to be sectioned [under section 5.2 of the Mental Health Act], which meant she had to be forcibly kept in hospital – but sometimes it would happen suddenly. Knowing Sarah could die any day made me realise what mattered in life – to have Sarah healthy was more important to me than any glories at work.

If I thought she was becoming ill, for instance if she was withdrawn or I came home and found an empty bottle of wine (drinking was the only thing that could blot out the voices), I'd pick her up at the end of the day so she wouldn't go off on her own. But sometimes I had to go away on business and I was never quite sure what would've happened by the time I returned.

Three years ago I reached breaking point. I'd never thought of leaving her, but I felt she wasn't being sensible about her lifestyle and I couldn't watch her every move. Somehow it seemed to get through to her because she began to take more responsibility for the illness herself. I realised I was carrying a lot of her illness for her, giving her the caring that she needed to develop for herself.

I've never been to any support groups for families of schizophrenics. My brother has always been there for me, and my boss knows about Sarah and gives me time off when she's ill. Sarah's parents, on the other hand, are quite frightened of mental illness, and anyway, they just think you should get on with things.

When we married I never expected that we'd have to cope with mental illness. It's meant our lives have been limited. We often had to cancel arrangements because Sarah was ill, but she's improved so much recently that we can begin to plan things again.

At the moment we don't want children because Sarah might become ill and not be able to look after them. They would also have a 15 per cent chance of developing the illness. Anyway, we've found we can put that extra energy into supporting mental health campaigns. Since Sarah's been ill I've developed strong ideas on the subject. I think everyone needs to be better educated about mental illness. There should be more money put into supplying beds, more co-operation between sufferers and psychiatrists over the medication, but, most of all, people should realise that the mentally ill are human beings. Sarah's a person not an illness.
Names and places have been changed.
© New Woman
January, 1996

Mental illness

What can you do about it?

A different response for different needs

Just as there are many different types of physical illness, mental illness comes in many different forms as well. Similarly, if someone develops a problem with their mental health, they remain as individual from other people as they were before. In each case, the treatment and help that are available should take into account the individual needs of the people involved.

It is not helpful to talk of someone as being a 'depressive', a 'neurotic', or a 'schizophrenic'. Not only can it be misleading to use these terms to describe someone who is experiencing mental health problems, it is not helpful to pigeon-hole people in this way.

There will be similarities between what affects one person and what affects another, but any help offered should focus on the individual and his or her unique background and circumstances.

If you feel that something may be wrong

Everyone needs someone who will take the time and trouble to listen when there are problems or worries. Family, employers and friends are especially important sources of support – sometimes a talk with them may be all that is needed.

Your family doctor is there to help

But when things are a bit more serious or won't go away, you may need to contact your family doctor. His or her understanding and assistance can be invaluable. Doctors themselves or a counsellor, psychologist or nurse in their practice can often provide the help needed. Voluntary organisations and self-help groups like the Samaritans, or CRUSE when a bereavement has taken place, are also a source of help. In these ways, the majority of anxieties and feelings of depression are helped without the need for specialist care.

The mental health team

Psychiatric or mental health services can sometimes add to or enhance the care offered by your doctor. Mental health nurses, psychologists, psychiatrists, occupational therapists and social workers all have special skills and facilities they can use to help you. Together these specialists work as a mental health team.

The role of the key worker

If you do see a specialist from a mental health team, you should be offered one person who will be your main contact – your key worker. Depending on what help you need, you may have several members of the mental health team to help you, but there should always be one key worker to whom you, your spouse or carer, and your family doctor can turn if they need information or to get help promptly. If you need help from just one member of the team, that person will normally be your key worker. It is important to let the mental health team know if you would prefer your key worker to be someone of the same sex or culture as you, if that is possible.

Working out a care plan

Your care needs should be carefully assessed. A plan to meet these needs – a care plan – can then be drawn up

by the key worker and you, often with advice from other members of the mental health team. For you to be helped most effectively, this care plan should be worked out with your help. If you are not happy with part of it, then or subsequently, your key worker will discuss it with you and try to take on board your concerns and wishes.

Other people involved with your care, such as your family doctor, social worker and relatives or carer, should also be involved in putting together your care plan after discussion with you. You should then be given a copy of the plan so that you have a record of what has been agreed. If your needs change, your care plan should reflect this.

This method of working is called the care programme approach, which has been developed to make mental health services more flexible and effective. It ensures that everyone who comes to the mental health services for help:

- has their needs assessed;
- is provided with a key worker;
- receives a care plan;
- has their care needs reviewed when needed.

What is care management?

In a similar fashion, people with complex social care needs – not necessarily involving mental health problems – can also receive a carefully tailored package of care from their local authority social services department; this is called care management.

A person with mental health problems, and his or her carer or family, can approach the social services department and ask to have their social care needs assessed. This type of care would be in addition to the care programme worked out with the mental health team to meet mental health needs, but both types of help would be co-ordinated so that the person receives the right combination.

Will I be labelled as 'mental' if I seek help for a mental health problem? Don't I just need to pull myself together?

If it was as easy as just pulling yourself together, you would surely have done so by now. Don't hesitate to seek help if you feel there is something wrong. The important thing to remember is that you are not alone. One in eight people goes to their family doctor to talk about emotional problems each year, and at least a million people see members of mental health teams. The mental health team is there to help you as an individual, not to label you. It is far better to get help early if you need it than to wait until things are really bad. There is no evidence that you can see a specialist too early but there is plenty to suggest that if you wait, it makes things more difficult. You also need to take into account the needless suffering you may go through.

So what can be done?

There are effective ways of dealing with feelings of distress, including:

Talking treatments

When things are getting you down, it can be invaluable to be able to talk about them with someone who can help you understand what is happening to you:

- it may let you talk about how you feel and simply by letting you put things in words help to make sense of your problems;
- it may allow you to understand why you feel the way you do, and perhaps to accept that the feelings you have are quite reasonable in your particular circumstances or after what has happened to you;
- they may help you work out a plan of action so that you can do something positive about the problems you have;
- it may help you to go over the thoughts you are having and see whether they have been making things worse – perhaps you are being too critical of yourself.

Medication

Different forms of medication are available and can be very helpful when you have become depressed or 'mixed-up.'

- Anti-depressants can help you regain the motivation to tackle any problems you have. Even though being depressed may be perfectly understandable in your particular circumstances, your doctor may still suggest anti-depressants as a way of helping you cope better. Anti-depressants are NOT addictive. Tranquillizers, however, can be addictive and are used much less frequently now than in the past.
- Neuroleptics such as haloperidol or chlorpromazine are sometimes used as tranquillizers but usually only for people suffering from hypomania ('getting high') or schizophrenia. They help to reduce agitation, assist sleep and ease specific symptoms like hearing voices (hallucinations), paranoia and other beliefs that have become out of proportion to the sufferer's situation.
- ECT. Occasionally when people have become very depressed, it can be hard for them to motivate themselves even enough to eat and drink. In such a life-threatening situation, electroconvulsive therapy – or ECT – is a very safe treatment which can help the person begin to recover quickly.

While recovering, it may also be helpful to have somewhere special to go in the day, such as day-centres, day hospitals, clubs and drop-in centres. Sometimes having somewhere special to stay overnight is also a useful option. Most psychiatric wards are now in district general hospitals and, if you need care and support at night, can provide a period of support and safety over 24 hours. Many districts are developing these facilities in the community, away from hospitals; sometimes there are also hospital hostels.

For some people, care and support may be needed over a few months or years, and most health districts are now developing a range of staffed and supported accommo-dation for them to replace the care that was previously provided in psychiatric hospitals.

Sources of help

When someone develops mental health problems, it is then that they most need support and acceptance. To summarise what has been mentioned already, there are many sources of help.

Voluntary groups

Organisations like the Samaritans, CRUSE, MIND or NSF can help you. You may find that there are other counselling groups available locally or at your college or workplace.

Family doctors

Family doctors and their teams can be particularly helpful. They are involved in arranging care for more people with mental health problems than any other group of professionals.

Social workers

Social workers can also provide care and assistance, particularly with the practical problems of daily living as well as problems within families. Most social services departments will also have specialist mental health social workers who can be asked for assistance if needed.

Mental health team

Your family doctor or social worker may suggest that you see someone from the mental health team of nurses, psychologists, psychiatrists, occupational therapists and social workers. Their role is to offer you specialist help if your situation is not improving or is getting worse.

But all sorts of people can provide help in many different ways, such as:

- doctors or nurses in casualty departments or general hospitals;
- people working in housing departments, DSS benefits offices, employment offices, the police or courts;
- neighbours, friends at work, or the company welfare office;
- virtually everybody may be able to help, if only to recognise that something is wrong and to help someone to get further assistance.

© Department of Health
March, 1996

SANE

What is it and what does it do?

SANE is a campaigning organisation which was established in 1986 following the overwhelming response to a series of articles by Marjorie Wallace in *The Times* entitled 'The Forgotten Illness'. Its focus was initially on schizophrenia – Schizophrenia a national emergency – but has expanded to cover all forms of mental illness.

One family in four is affected by mental illness – it is as common as heart disease, three times more common than cancer and five times more common than learning disability. It is one of the top three causes of sick leave and costs British industry £3.7 billion every year. SANE, which was founded in 1986 to meet the challenge of mental illness, is committed to action.

What does Saneline offer to callers?

What Saneline offers

Saneline not only offers emotional support but also information and help in five key areas:

- statutory, voluntary and independent mental health services on both a local and national basis;
- medication, treatments and side effects;
- psychological treatments and other therapies;
- illnesses and symptoms;
- mental health law and sufferer and carer rights.

Saneline's unique database

The volunteer first of all listens to the caller to absorb and assess what action might help. Using the Saneline database, which is indexed by nearest large town (or borough in London), the volunteer can access detailed descriptions of services provided in the caller's own area.

The quality of this national database with over 12,000 entries is maintained through continual checking and updating.

Through our analysis of (confidential) log sheets we can establish the most urgent needs of both people with mental illness and their carers. As we are working on samples in excess of 18,000 from people both receiving help and those who have never contacted, or have lost touch with, the services, we are able to highlight gaps in community and health care policy. This enables us to inform those in charge of mental health services and to lobby government for improvements.

We work closely with the Samaritans, ChildLine, mental health and other charities many of whom have their services listed on the database.

Using our experience we have forged links with organisations such as the police, the Benefits Agency, companies and other organisations to provide staff training on mental health awareness.

Caller care and professional advice

If callers have a problem which involves the need for professional

expertise we have consultant psychiatrists who are willing to give second opinions; we have experts in social services and a Legal Information Manager, a barrister with ten years' experience recently appointed to the Mental Health Act Commission. She is supported by 150 lawyers throughout the UK who are prepared to give half an hour free advice and, in some circumstances, to follow up cases.

The vision of Saneline is to move people from a position where they feel helpless into the best network of care. In addition callers whose crises cannot be dealt with immediately can be followed up by our Caller Care Manager who keeps in touch through periods of critical distress and maintains ongoing support.

At any one time 15% of our callers phone us regularly.

Who calls Saneline?

The majority of calls is from sufferers – 57% – whilst carers account for 34%. It is interesting to note the gender split:

- for sufferers, 48% are male and 52% female
- for carers, 23% are male and 77% female

What are the illnesses they were calling about?

- Schizophrenia   40.3%
- Depression   33.3%
- Manic Depression   11.2%
- Anxiety   5.1%
- Phobia   1.3%
- Other   8.8%

Of all the callers, 20% have suicidal thoughts. More than half of them have attempted suicide before and 2% of all callers are in the act of taking their lives at the time of their call.

© SANE

What are child and adolescent psychiatrists?

Information from Young Minds – the children's mental health charity

Child and Adolescent Psychiatrists are medically qualified doctors who specialise in understanding and working with the mental health problems of children and young people

The training of consultant child and adolescent psychiatrists (or child psychiatrists for short) includes three years working in mental health services and four years specialising in work with children, young people and their families.

Other psychiatrists who are not as senior as consultants may be called registrars or specialist registrars. They are usually quite senior doctors who have spent many years in practice but are still acquiring further experience and training in order to become highly-qualified specialists.

Where do they work?

Within the National Health Service, child psychiatrists mainly work in child and family consultation centres or child guidance clinics, outpatient clinics and in hospitals. They work as part of a team with other child mental health professionals such as psychologists, psychotherapists, psychiatric nurses and social workers. Most of the work they do with children and their families is carried out through out-patient contact, that is, the child continues to live at home. Child psychiatrists also work in units where children who need more help and care spend time as inpatients or attend each day over a period of time. They also often work in child development clinics, student health services, day nurseries and family centres. They are sometimes asked to provide expert opinion to the courts.

What sort of problems can they help with?

Child psychiatrists deal with a wide range of children's and young people's mental health problems. These are emotional and behavioural problems that trouble children and cause worry to those who care for them – family and friends may no longer feel able to make sense of the problems or know how to manage them. Some of these problems can be very disturbing, ending up with children feeling very confused or out of control. Some children may become withdrawn and fearful; others more outgoing and aggressive. Problems may show themselves at school – being disruptive, having difficulty in concentrating, refusing to attend school; or they may be more private – preoccupied with food, not sleeping well or becoming depressed or self-destructive. The reasons why they feel and behave the way they do may be very complex and so may need several assessment sessions.

Typical problems seen by child psychiatrists are:

In under-5s:
– communication problems
– odd or unusual behaviour
– sleep problems
– difficult behaviour
– excessive clinging and fears
– delays in development

School children:
– aggressive or disruptive behaviour
– hyperactive behaviour
– psychosomatic symptoms (stress-related aches and pains)
– anxieties, phobias and compulsions
– school attendance difficulties
– soiling and wetting
– repeated stealing and lying
– excessive anti-social and aggressive behaviour
– emotional problems interfering with school work

– friend/relationship problems
– family problems

Teenagers:
– eating disorders
– relationship problems with friends or family, e.g. withdrawing from social activities or always falling out with friends
– sexual orientation problems
– psychosomatic problems
– depression
– suicidal behaviour
– self-damaging behaviour
– substance abuse

Child psychiatrists also help a small number of children who have severe behavioural and emotional problems – e.g. autism, Asperger's Syndrome, Attention Deficit Hyperactivity Disorder and, in older children, severe mental illness such as schizophrenia.

How do child and adolescent psychiatrists work?

A large part of a child psychiatrist's work is to identify the problem, find out the causes and give advice about what may help. They take into account a range of factors that may lead to these difficulties – including the child's family, school or community as well as their medical and psychological background. They carry out their assessments by interviewing the child and his or her family, and through information from schools, and other doctors or professionals who may have contact with the child (with the parent's and child's agreement).

On the basis of their assessments, child psychiatrists, together with their colleagues, provide different kinds of help for the child and family. This may be individual, group or family therapy. It may include talking with children about the thoughts and feelings that are upsetting them, and helping parents and others to understand and manage better a child's difficult behaviour better. The child psychiatrist may also take a leading role in advising and helping other professionals plan how best to help the child and the family. They sometimes prescribe medication and a few children with more serious conditions may need admission to hospital, but most children who are seen by child psychiatrists are helped as out-patients in ordinary clinics.

How can my child see a psychiatrist?

Your family doctor, school doctor, clinic doctor or a paediatrician will be able to discuss any concerns and arrange for you to see a child psychiatrist. Some child and family consultation services will accept referral from parents.

Young Minds Parents Information Service can tell you about help in your area, including local child and family consultation services (child guidance clinics). You can contact Young Minds Parents Information Service at Young Minds, 102-108 Clerkenwell Road, London, EC1M 5SA. Tel: 0171 336 8445. Fax: 0171 336 8446, Parents Information Service: 0345 626376

How to help someone who is suicidal

Why do people become suicidal?

'When I grew up and things went particularly badly, I used to say to myself, over and over . . . "I wish I were dead" . . . Then one day I understood what I was saying. I was walking along the edge of Hampstead Heath after some standard domestic squabble, and suddenly I heard the phrase for the first time. I stood still to attend to the words. I repeated them slowly, listening. And realised that I meant it.'

A.Alvarez. *The Savage God – A Study of Suicide*. Penguin, 1983

The reasons why people become suicidal involve a complex mix of individual and social factors. Hopeless and desperate feelings have many sources. Sudden personal crises may trigger despair. A run of problems or bad luck may feel overwhelming. Or despair may mount slowly as the pressures and hurts of many years wear down a person's self-esteem. A 'last straw' incident or problem may precede a suicide attempt, but this is often not the real cause. Just as a sense of despair takes years to build up, suicidal feelings often develop gradually.

The more pain one feels the more one needs to know that there is a way of stopping it. So as life becomes more distressing and difficult to bear, the thought of

death may grow more appealing. Personal beliefs about what death will bring – nothingness, a place in heaven, reunion with the dead, reincarnation – may bring comfort. People in a suicidal crisis often feel powerless because the events and pressures in their life seem to be beyond their control. When one is

feeling helpless and hopeless it may be comforting to think that death is still under our control.

Someone who has thought about suicide in the past, however vaguely and periodically, is more likely to resort to it as a means of coping when life becomes stressful. Many people may experience

Suicide in the UK

Thirteen people commit suicide every day

Suicides involving mental illness 90%

Other reasons for suicides 10%

Source: Mental Illness: The Fundamental Facts, The Mental Health Foundation

suicidal feelings without acting on them. They may come and go according to the stresses and strains one experiences.

Who becomes suicidal?

'I'm writing to ask for help. I'm a Muslim girl and when I was ten I was badly abused by a family friend. I've never told anyone. Since then I've kept myself to myself and have tried to take overdoses of Paracetamol. Whenever I'm at home with the family I'm scared and feel lonely. I'd like to leave my family and start afresh. I'm over 18. What should I do? At the moment I feel like doing SOMETHING I should have done years ago, which is to stab myself.'

A reader's letter in My Guy
11.7.1992

Many people reach a stage in their life when they feel they can no longer cope or see any point in going on. These feelings are surprisingly common but some groups of people appear particularly vulnerable to suicidal feelings. The incidence of suicide in people diagnosed with a serious mental health problem such as manic depression or schizophrenia is considerably higher than in the general population and has been estimated as being in the region of 15 per cent. Suicidal thoughts may be linked to delusional ideas, but the most important factor which could lead someone who has a serious mental health problem to take their own life may be a lack of social

> *Asian women between 15 and 24 years of age have a suicide rate which is almost three times higher than the national average*

support and a sense of hopelessness about the future.

It is reckoned that one in seven people who suffer from severe depression will die by suicide and that the majority of seriously depressed people will experience intense suicidal thoughts. Psychological factors and external situations and events may interlock to precipitate a suicide attempt. There is a strong association between the recent experience of negative life events and suicide and attempted suicide, as well as the onset of depression.

Dependence on alcohol and drugs also increases the risk of suicide. In turn these difficulties may reflect life experiences which have been particularly painful and traumatic such as sexual abuse and early bereavement.

Research into suicide statistics demonstrates that there is a link between suicide and wider social

factors. Suicide is twice as common in men as in women. However, increasing numbers of women are attempting suicide. Deliberate overdosing has become the major reason for emergency medical admissions of women to hospital. Asian women between 15 and 24 years of age have a suicide rate which is almost three times higher than the national average. Immigrant status increases the risk of suicide and attempted suicide.

Relationships matter

A common cause of suicide is the break-up of a relationship. Recently, the highest suicide rates for men aged 15-44 have been among those who were single, divorced or widowed. These men have suicide rates which are about three times higher than those of married men. It is probably no coincidence that St Valentine's Day, the date which in most people's minds is connected with an idealised romantic view of relationships, is associated with a rise in attempted suicide.

Age matters

There has been a 50 per cent increase in the number of suicides among men under 25 in the past ten years. Every year one girl in 100 attempts suicide. Research suggests that relationship problems are the most frequent difficulty particularly for girls, with unemployment, alcohol and drug problems also being common,

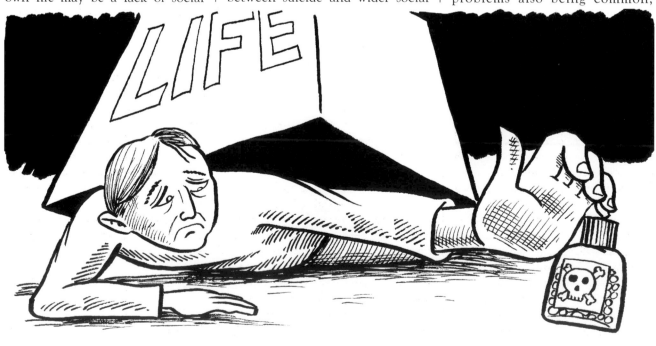

especially in males. There is strong evidence to suggest that lesbian and gay young people are particularly at risk of attempting or committing suicide. In addition it was reported in August 1994 that a record number of young offenders aged 20 and under have killed themselves in jail. Many teenagers are traumatised by conditions in custody where bullying is rife.

Elderly people are also at risk with bereavement, loneliness, loss of role and status and ill health being contributory factors. Incapacitating, painful physical disease increases suicide risk.

Occupation matters

Links between unemployment rates and the frequency of suicidal behaviour among young adults have been clearly demonstrated. Rises in the general male suicide rate have been shown to be associated with rises in unemployment.

Some occupations appear to be more likely to induce suicidal feelings. Compared to the average person, farmers are nearly twice as likely to kill themselves and their suicide rate is fourth highest behind vets, dentists and pharmacists. Suicide rates in rural Wales, the uplands of Scotland and the remotest parts of Devon and Cornwall are as high as in deprived inner-city areas of London. The stress of farming as big business, financial problems, isolation and the humiliations of failure are some of the factors which could account for the plague of rural suicides.

Don't people have a right to kill themselves if they want to?

'A part of me always knew he was dying even though his body remained alive despite eight suicide attempts. The agony he experienced had caused a kind of death inside already and however much he struggled to believe that life could win through, ultimately it could not and he made his choice accordingly. He faced that choice with courage, strength and a great deal of love and humour in his actions and words towards others.'

Bushy Kelly writing about her brother's suicide. 'In the face of death' in OPENMIND 39

Some people make repeated suicide attempts and appear to express a strong, unambivalent wish for death. One carer's reaction on being told of her son's death was, 'Thank goodness for that'. Family and friends may come to accept that death is the inevitable outcome of so much emotional anguish. They may feel relieved that the person will not have to face further suffering.

However, many people are far more ambivalent, and suicidal feelings may come and go according to the stresses and strains in their day-to-day-lives. For many people there are likely to be less extreme ways of resolving problems. Even when someone appears to be absolutely determined to take their own life, the importance of talking and examining every possible option and source of support cannot be over-estimated. It is important to encourage the person not to view suicide as the only possible solution.

How can I help someone who feels that bad?

'After he made the first two suicide attempts in the space of 24 hours, I felt completely wiped out. My overwhelming feeling was that it must be so awful being married to me, he'd rather be dead.'

A reader in OPENMIND 65

The two chief concerns which you are likely to have if you are trying to help someone who is suicidal are about their immediate safety and the causes of their desperation. It is important to encourage the person to talk about their despairing feelings and not to dismiss expressions of hopelessness as a 'cry for help' or try to jolly them out of it. Talking openly about the possibility of suicide will not make it more likely to happen.

Just being there for the person and listening in an accepting way could contribute to making them feel less isolated and frightened.

At the same time, if you are in a close relationship with them you are likely to feel fearful, angry or guilty. You will need to find someone – whether a friend, family member, a professional, the Samaritans, or a carers' support group – in whom you can confide

your fears. It is also important to persuade the suicidal person to get some outside support

The GP is a good starting-point for professional help and may be able to arrange for other help such as counselling to be made available or to prescribe anti-depressants if appropriate.

It may be useful to emphasise to the suicidal person that overdosing with certain drugs will not be an easy answer to all their problems. Over-dosing can lead to messy, painful and long-drawn-out consequences such as slow poisoning.

It is important to discuss strategies for seeking help when suicidal thoughts occur. Creating a personal support list is a useful way of reviewing every conceivable option. The list may include the names, phone numbers and addresses of individuals, helplines, organisations and professionals available to someone should they need support. Persuade the person to keep this list by the phone and to agree to call someone on the list when they are feeling suicidal.

For a young person who has expressed suicidal feelings, drawing up such a list is in itself a sign of care and concern. Often young people may resist sharing their personal feelings and problems. If they are reluctant to seek outside help, the information may provide food for thought, allowing them the option of seeking help when they feel ready. Do not neglect yourself: you should compile your own list to ensure that your needs for support and advice are met.

Surviving or diffusing a suicidal crisis is one thing, solving underlying problems another. The difficulties that nurture despair are usually complex and do not vanish quickly. It is essential to address these underlying problems or suicidal feelings may well return. Seeking help with the problems that have led to suicidal unhappiness will represent the starting-point of a lengthy process.

• The above is an extract from How to . . . help someone who is suicidal, produced by MIND. See page 39 for address details. © MIND, 1997

INDEX

abuse, and mental health problems 18-19
adolescents *see* young people
Alzheimer's disease 3, 23-5
    carers and care costs 25
    causes 25
    diagnosis 24, 25
    drugs for 23
    symptoms 24
    treatment 25
anorexia nervosa 3
anti-depressants 32, 37
anxiety 3
    and depression 14
    and young people 4
Asian women, and suicidal
        behaviour 36

boys, suicidal behaviour 10, 12-13
bulimia nervosa 3

care programmes 31-2
carers
    of dementia sufferers 22, 25
    and suicidal behaviour 37
child psychiatrists 34-5
children
    and depression 2, 9-10
    and mental health 3-4
    and suicidal behaviour 10, 12-13
    see also young people

dementia 3, 7, 21
    statistics 21, 23, 24
    symptoms 22, 24
    see also Alzheimer's disease
depression 2, 14-17
    causes of 14-15
    in children 2, 9-10
    dealing with 15-16
    endogenous 14
    and older people 21-2
    physical causes of 15
    post-natal 14, 20-1
    statistics 8, 9, 16
    and suicidal behaviour 13, 36
    symptoms 2, 14, 16
    treatments 16-17
    in the workplace 16-17
    in young people 2, 4, 5-6, 13
discrimination, and mental health
        problems 18-19

eating disorders 3, 34
employees, mental health education
        for 17

families
    and child depression 9-10
    and child psychiatrists 34-5
    and mental health problems 4,
        7-8
    and schizophrenia 27, 30
    treatments 27
family doctors *see* GPs (general
        practitioners)

gender differences *see* sex differences
girls, suicidal behaviour 10, 12-13,
        36-7
GPs (general practitioners) 31, 32, 37
    and older people 22

harassment, and mental health
        problems 18-19
heart disease, and schizophrenia 28
helplines 6, 8, 33

job dissatisfaction, and stress 17

magnesium, and schizophrenia 28
manic-depressive illness 2, 7, 14
ME (Myalgic Encephalomyelitis) 15
medication 32, 37
    for Alzheimer's disease 23
    and child psychiatrists 35
men
    and depression 16
    and neurotic disorders 8
    and suicidal behaviour 36
mental health teams 31-2
mental illness
    causes of 1
    statistics 1, 5, 7
mothers
    and child depression 9
    and post-natal depression 14,
        20-1

'nervous breakdown' 1
neurosis 2

obsessions, and young people 4
obsessive compulsive disorder 7, 8
older people 21-5
    carers of 22
    and depression 21-2
    statistics 21

parents
    and causes of depression 14
    and childhood mental health
problems 4
personality disorders 3

post-natal depression 14, 20-1
psychoanalysts 10-11
psychosis 1-2
    and young people 3

schizophrenia 2, 7, 26-30
    and bodily diseases 27-8
    causes 27
    diagnosis 26
    living with 28-30
    nutritional factors in 28
    and Saneline 33
    and suicidal behaviour 36
    symptoms 26-7
    treatments 28, 29
school phobia 4, 34
self-harm
    and schizophrenia sufferers 29
    and young people 5, 13
self-help groups 31
sex differences
    neurotic disorders 8
    suicidal behaviour 12-13, 36
social workers 32
stress experiences
    and depression in the workplace
        17
    and suicidal behaviour 13
suicidal behaviour 35-7
    in children and young people 6,
        10, 12-13
    international differences 13
    and Saneline 33
    and schizophrenia 29
    statistics 10, 12, 13, 35

teenagers *see* young people

unemployment, and suicidal
        behaviour 37

women
    and depression 15, 16
    and neurotic disorders 8

Young Minds Parents' Information
        Service 35
young people
    and depression 2, 4, 5-6
    helplines for 6, 8
    and mental health 3-8
    and psychosis 3
    and schizophrenia 27
    self-harm 5, 13
    suicidal behaviour 6, 10, 12-13,
        36-7

ADDITIONAL RESOURCES

Alzheimer's Disease Society
Gordon House
10 Greencoat Place
London, SW1P 1PH
Tel: 0171 306 0606
Fax: 0171 306 0808
The leading care and research charity for people with Alzheimer's Disease and other forms of dementia and their families.

Association for Post-Natal Illness
25 Jerdan Place
Fulham
London, SW6 1BE
Tel: 0171 386 0868
Fax: 0171 386 8885
Advises and supports women suffering from post-natal depression. Produces publications.

Careline
Cardinal Heenan Centre
326 High Road
Ilford, IG1 1QP
Tel: 0181 514 5444
Careline: 0181 514 1177
Careline provides confidential telephone counselling for children, young people and adults. It offers a unique service in that it can provide counselling to any individual on any issue.

Manic Depression Fellowship Ltd
8-10 High Street
Kingston upon Thames
Surrey, KT1 1EY
Tel: 0181 974 6550
Fax: 0181 974 6600
Provides support, advice and information for people with manic depression, their families, friends and carers. Produces publications.

Mental Health Foundation
37 Mortimer Street
London, W1N 8JU
Tel: 0171 580 0145
Fax: 0171 631 3868
Works to prevent mental disorder wherever possible by funding and supporting research and educating people about the causes and effects.

MIND
Granta House
15-19 Broadway
London, E15 4BQ
Tel: 0181 519 2122
Fax: 0181 522 1725
MIND is a leading mental health charity in England and Wales. Produces a wide range of advice leaflets (45p each), reports and books. Has recently published *How to recognise the early signs of mental distress*, price £1 from Mind Publications. Ask for their publications list. Also produce the magazine *OpenMind*

National Children's Bureau
8 Wakely Street
London, EC1V 7QE
Tel: 0171 843 6000
Fax: 0171 278 9512
Provides information on children's needs in the family, school and society. Publishes a series of factsheets called *Highlights*.

NCH Action for Children
85 Highbury Park
London, N5 1UD
Tel: 0171 226 2033
Fax: 0171 226 2537
One of the UK's leading childcare charities with 250 projects nationwide helping over 25,000 children and young people every year.

Royal College of Psychiatrists
17 Belgrave Square
London, SW1X 8PG
Tel: 0171 235 2351
Fax: 0171 245 1231
Produces an excellent series of free leaflets on various aspects of mental health. Supplied free of charge but a stamped, addressed envelope is required.

SANE
2nd Floor
199-205 Old Marylebone Road
London, NW1 5QP
Tel: 0171 724 6520
Fax: 0171 724 6502

SANE runs the first national telephone helpline providing relief to sufferers, support to carers and information to healthcare professionals. Ask for their publications list.

Schizophrenia Association of Great Britain (SAGB)
International Schizophrenia Centre
Bryn Hyfryd
The Cresent
Bangor
Gwynedd, LL57 2AG
Tel: 01248 354048
Helps and advises people with schizophrenia and their families.

The Samaritans
10 The Grove
Slough, SL1 1QP
Tel: 01753 532713
The Samaritans provide confidential, emotional support for anyone in crisis who may be dispairing or suicidal, 24-hours a day on 0345 909090 for the price of a local call.

World Mental Health Day
Health Education Authority
Hamilton House
Mabledon Place
London, WC1H 9TX
Tel: 0171 413 1991
Fax: 0171 388 4608
World Mental Health Day is celebrated annually on 10th October. The Health Education Authority co-ordinates the World Mental Health Day Campaign. The campaign guide, *Positive Steps*, is available from the above telephone number.

Young Minds
102-108 Clerkenwell Road
London, EC1M 5SA
Tel: 0171 336 8445
Fax: 0171 336 8446
Young Minds, the national association for children's mental health. Produces a range of leaflets, reports, magazines and newsletters.

ACKNOWLEDGEMENTS

The publisher is grateful for permission to reproduce the following material.

While every care has been taken to trace and acknowledge copyright, the publisher tenders its apology for any accidental infringement or where copyright has proved untraceable. The publisher would be pleased to come to a suitable arrangement in any such case with the rightful owner.

Chapter One: What is mental illness?

Mental illness, © HMSO Reproduced with the kind permission of Her Majesty's Stationery Office, March 1996, *Mental health and the young*, © The Mental Health Foundation, *Help! I'm losing control*, © Just 17, October 1996, *Mental health problems – what do they mean?*, © Young Minds, *Hidden signs of a depressed child*, © Telegraph Group Limited, London 1996, *'Crisis out of a drama' on unstable children*, © The Daily Mail, December 1996, *That old shrinking feeling*, © The Guardian, May 1996, *Suicidal behaviour in children and young people*, © National Children's Bureau, 1996, *Understanding depression*, © MIND, *Depression in the workplace*, © Royal College of Psychiatrists, HMSO Reproduced with the kind permission of Her Majesty's Stationery Office, *Not just sticks and stones*, © MIND, November 1996, *The baby blues and postnatal depression*, ©

Association for Post-natal Illness, *Mental health and older people*, © Mental Health Foundation, *Drug that can ease the misery of Alzheimer's*, © The Daily Mail, January 1997, *Dementia in perspective*, © Alzheimer's Disease Society, *Alzheimer's disease – what is it?*, © Alzheimer's Disease Society, May 1996, *The cost of caring*, © Centre for Socio-Legal Studies, 1995, *Can you tell me something about schizophrenia?*, © The Schizophrenia Association of Great Britain (SAGB), *Living with schizophrenia*, © New Woman, January 1996.

Chapter Two: Seeking help

Mental illness, © HMSO Reproduced with the kind permission of Her Majesty's Stationery Office, March 1996, *SANE*, © SANE, *What are child and adolescent psychiatrists?*, © Young Minds, *How to help someone who is suicidal*, © MIND.

Photographs and Illustrations

Pages 2, 5, 10, 11, 19, 26, 36: Andrew Smith, pages 22, 24, 29: Michaela Bloomfield.

Craig Donnellan
Cambridge
September, 1997